NUCLEUS

A TRIP INTO THE HEART OF MATTER

NUCLEUS
A TRIP INTO THE HEART OF MATTER
RAY MACKINTOSH, JIM AL-KHALILI, BJÖRN JONSON AND TERESA PEÑA

Second Edition

Dundee University Press

Originally published in 2001

Second edition published 2011

Printed in China

9 8 7 6 5 4 3 2 1

Dundee University Press
University of Dundee
Nethergate
Dundee
DD1 4HN
www.dundee.ac.uk/dup

978-1-84586-131-5

Acknowledgements

The authors are most grateful to the European Physical Society (EPS) and the Nuclear Physics European Collaboration Committee (NuPECC) who have generously and patiently supported this project. In particular, we wish to thank Jules Deutsch, Adriaan van der Woude, Alan Shotter, Christoph Bargholtz, Sissy Körner and all the other members of PANS who have given us their support and advice. We are also grateful to the EU for support under the Fifth Framework programme. Björn Jonson thanks the Nobel Committee for Physics for support and Raymond Mackintosh is grateful to Dr Sean Ryan for helpful advice with the astronomy. Jim Al-Khalili is grateful to Walter Gilboy, Simon Doran and William Gelletly for useful comments on nuclear applications. Teresa Peña thanks José Carvalho Soares, Fernanda Silva, Teresa Pinheiro and Luis Cerqueira for information about applications of nuclear physics and Ariel Guerreiro for general comments. Finally, we are grateful to David Jenkins, Dave Ireland, Peter Jones, and John Roberts and the Nuclear Institute, without whose assistance this new edition would not have been possible.

To
Marjorie and Ethan
Julie, David and Kate
Ann-Sophie, Anna, Sandra and Linn
Alfred and João

Contents

Foreword

In the closing years of the 1800s, Henri Becquerel, in Paris, discovered that uranium salts caused photographic plates to become fogged, even when they were wrapped in opaque layers of paper and kept in a dark drawer. This fogging was caused by new kinds of high energy rays coming spontaneously and continuously from the uranium atoms. These rays provided the first hint of the existence of a tiny particle, the 'atomic nucleus', located deep in the centre of every atom. An enormous scientific effort has been exerted during the past 100 years in order to study and to understand the fascinating new form of matter occurring in the atomic nuclei. This knowledge has made it possible to exploit a vast variety of practical applications of nuclear processes that profoundly contribute to the tools employed in other scientific disciplines (chemistry, astronomy and cosmology, biology, medicine, geology, and much more) as well as to practical industrial problems.

Because of the intrinsic interest and important societal role of nuclear science, it is most welcome that in this book a team of distinguished scientists who work at the forefront of current developments in this field use everyday language and exploit a wealth of informative pictures to explain the science and practical applications to a broad public.

Professor Ben Mottelson
Copenhagen

Preface

Since the first edition of *Nucleus: a Trip into the Heart of Matter* was published in 2001, there has been real progress in understanding atomic nuclei, the processes involving them and the applications of these processes, not the least of which are medical applications. This progress, together with the gratifying response to the first edition, which was translated into several foreign languages, motivated us to embark on a new edition. The overall structure of the book is the same, as is the story we tell. However, there is some new material reflecting advances that have been made, and every page has had improvements in content and presentation. In particular, the selection of pictures has been updated where required. The second edition links the illustrations more closely to the text in a way that we hope will be helpful to the reader. I would like to thank David Jenkins in York, and Peter Jones in Birmingham for their assistance. Finally, I am deeply grateful to Robin Rees for his enormous efforts in producing this book.

Ray Mackintosh
Milton Keynes, June 2011

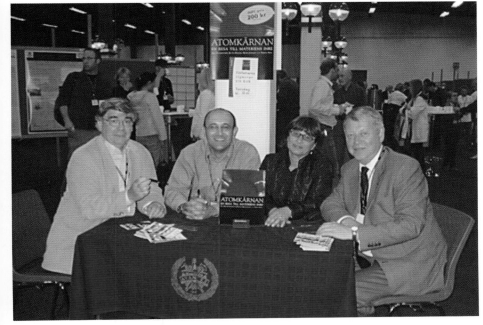

Atomkärnan

Left to right: Professors Ray Mackintosh, Jim Al-Khalili, Teresa Peña, and Björn Jonson, signing the first Swedish edition of the book at the INPC 2004 conference, organized by Professor Jonson and held in Göteborg, Sweden. The Swedish title is Atomkärnan.

Introduction
Our world and its infinite variety

Sun, sky, trees, the hum of insects, birds swooping high above – we live in a beautiful world of amazing variety. Yet our world also has another kind of beauty: the beauty that comes from an extraordinary unity lying behind the kaleidoscope of images. This 'unity' is quite straightforward, but it has taken thousands of years of human endeavour to uncover.

This book is about the human journey to the very heart of matter. The idea that everything in the world is made from the same few fundamental ingredients goes back a very long way. However, it has taken centuries to work out just what those fundamental ingredients are. We now know that all things around us, this book, the air we breathe, the stars at night, are made up of just a hundred or so different kinds of atoms. The variety comes about because the atoms combine in more ways than we would ever be able to count or even imagine.

It was the ancient Greek scientists, Leucippus and Democritus, who first conceived of atoms. The fact that water could freeze or turn into steam and then turn back into liquid again, struck them as deeply significant. What was it that stayed the same during these transformations? Their inspired guess was that everything was made of tiny, indivisible objects that kept their identity through transformations like melting and boiling. While we now know that atoms can be 'split', this process is rather extreme and is not done merely by heating mixtures of chemicals together. Leucippus and Democritus certainly had the right idea.

Our picture of atoms has changed since ancient times – their properties are not just a matter of colour or shape. We do not think of acids as being composed of sharp atoms, or copper made of reddish atoms, for example. Different types of atoms are associated with different substances; there are atoms of gold, atoms of carbon, and atoms of iron, for example, but there are no atoms of ice cream. Whereas some substances are composed purely of one particular type of atom, others, like ice cream, are more complex and are built from different varieties.

Empedocles, a Greek living in Sicily around 450 BC, put forward the idea that everything is made up from just four elements: earth, air, fire and water. This basic idea was a very good one, and certainly an advance on the suggestion of one of his predecessors, Thales, who proposed that everything was made of water. But even Thales was on the right track in looking for a fundamental ingredient to everything he could see. After a few thousand years of hard work, the number of elements identified has risen and is now approaching a hundred and twenty. Empedocles' earth, air, fire and water are not among them, but he had made a step along the right path. We now recognize that everything is made up of different combinations of elements, some familiar such as carbon, iron, hydrogen, oxygen; some exotic and, in some cases, extremely rare such as lutetium.

There are many questions to answer: *Where do these elements come from? Why are the proportions what they are? Why, for example is there much more carbon than gold?* The world might be prettier if gold predominated, but there would be no one to appreciate the glitter since carbon is the basis of life.

Many enthusiastic searchers for extraterrestrial life concede that it is unlikely any form of life exists in the Universe that is not based on carbon. In addition, carbon is not the only element that is essential to life; most life on Earth also needs hydrogen, oxygen, nitrogen and a dozen or so other elements. Our existence depends on them being in sufficient supply. So how did all these vital elements get here? The answer to this is one of the threads running through this book.

Another puzzle is why atoms have the particular properties that they do. We probably wouldn't exist if carbon atoms were as heavy as lead atoms, so why are they are so much lighter? This will be explained along with why there are only about a hundred elements and not a million, or just four as Empedocles supposed.

The origin of the Sun's energy

Vast energy produced by nuclear fusion at the centre of the Sun works its way out to the Sun's outer corona, producing remarkable displays in the ionized gas as it twists and turns in the Sun's incredibly powerful magnetic fields. This image was made by the space-based SOHO observatory's Extreme Ultraviolet Imaging Telescope. (SOHO/EIT Consortium, ESA, NASA)

In addition to investigating the composition of everything on Earth, this book looks outwards into the Cosmos. Our nearest star, the Sun, is indispensable for life on Earth. All our energy ultimately comes from the Sun: the energy that plants need for growing, the energy (occasionally released in spectacular lightning bolts) that drives the motion of the atmosphere; the energy that fuels all aspects of modern age of technology.

Around the beginning of the twentieth century it was discovered that the solar system was billions of years old. **The origin of the Sun's energy** then became an even greater mystery. What possible energy source could keep the Sun lit up for billions of years? No known source of heat came near to answering this. Now, over one hundred years later, that question can be answered. Why and how the Sun and the stars shine is another theme of this book.

To answer all the above questions we first need to understand the atomic nucleus, the tiny core at the centre of every atom. With that understanding, we can then appreciate how and where the nuclei were created. This will explain much about the world around us. We can also understand how energy is released by atomic nuclei when they transform from one kind to another. These transformations make it possible for the Sun to warm us, and are also a key to the entire life cycle of stars and the history of the Universe.

Perhaps the best known facts about atomic nuclei is that they are involved in horrifying bombs and in what is seen as an unfriendly way of making electricity. These issues are addressed too, and we attempt to explain the true nature of radioactivity, a natural nuclear process. Applications of nuclear processes, including radioactivity, are embedded in many aspects of our lives, from medicine to geology, from testing jet engines to smoke detectors. To take one example, when, some years ago, employees at a nuclear plant in Canada threatened to go on strike, it emerged that 47,000 medical procedures per day would have been threatened with cancellation.

Finally, how is it that we can be so confident that we know the age of the solar system? This is an example of how radioactivity has helped solve a riddle in an entirely different field. The key to dating the solar system was discovered just over one hundred years ago by Ernest Rutherford through his discoveries

The Crab Nebula

The Crab Nebula is a supernova remnant; most of the elements we know today were created in massive stellar explosions. (European Southern Observatories)

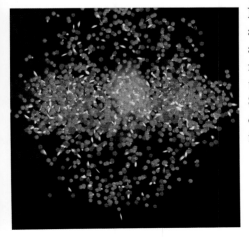

concerning the natural nuclear processes that occur in rocks. To this day, the same ideas play a key role in unravelling the history of our planet Earth.

The attempt to explain everything in terms of a single substance, which was started by so long ago by Thales, has now reached fruition. Today, we can describe the structure of all atomic nuclei in terms of an even smaller number of elementary particles.

Can nuclear fusion, the source of the Sun's energy, be harnessed on Earth to help satisfy humanity's energy needs? This is the hope of many scientists around the world who are working together to achieve this, see **Working towards fusion on Earth**. Nuclear fusion is presented in Chapter 9, which explains just how it comes about that nuclear fusion both warms us and produced the elements of which we are made. Sometimes these processes produce spectacular results, like the super-nova explosion that produced **The Crab nebula**. Spectacular as supernovae are, they are almost nothing compared to the Big Bang at the birth of our Universe: **Simulating the Big Bang** gives an impression of the production in the laboratory of the stuff the entire Universe was made of about a millionth of a second after the first instant of the Big Bang, the subject of the final chapter.

1. The size of things

From the immensity of space to the invisible world of the nucleus

Not so many generations ago, our ancestors would very likely have expressed the smallness of something by comparing it with a speck of dust floating in a shaft of sunlight. If they wanted to convey vastness, they might have made a comparison with a mountain, or even, if they were a little more sophisticated, with the Earth itself. If they were very learned, they might even have conjured up something a little larger: the sphere on which the 'fixed stars' were attached.

Today, our sense of the large and the small has expanded far beyond the comprehension of our forebears. This is due, at least in part, to the imaginative

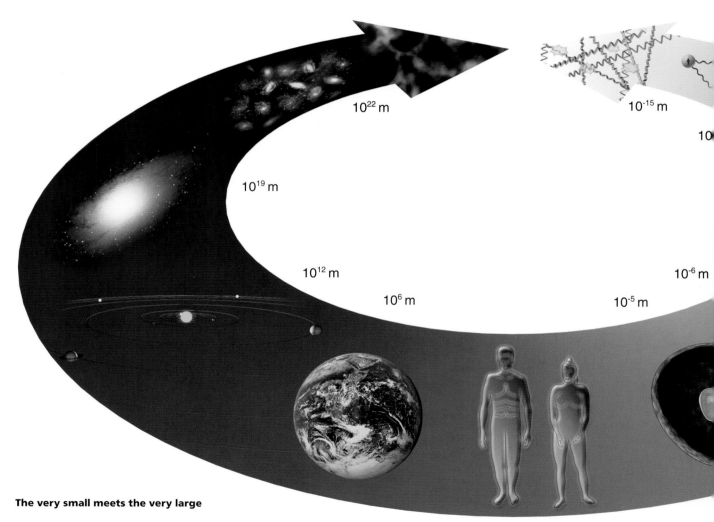

10^{22} m

10^{-15} m

10

10^{19} m

10^{12} m

10^{6} m

10^{-6} m

10^{-5} m

The very small meets the very large

People stand midway between the immensity of the Universe and the unimaginable smallness of atomic nuclei and their building blocks. Yet what happened long ago involving these tiniest of objects set the entire Universe on its course. Today, we cannot understand the Universe as a whole without understanding Nature on the smallest scale. That is why the largest and the smallest meet in this picture.

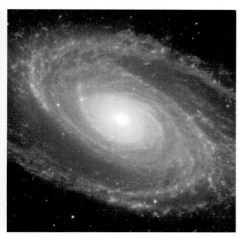

Spiral galaxy M81

M81 lies some 12 million light years from Earth and contains around 250 million stars. Some galaxies are clearly not spiral in form, such as the one at left in the diagram **The very small meets the very large.** This image is from the Spitzer Space Telescope, courtesy of NASA.

use of pieces of curved glass: the invention of the microscope and telescope. Our modern understanding of the Universe involves both the unimaginably large and the unimaginably small. The nucleus is minuscule, but understanding its properties helps us to comprehend some of the ideas about matter on the greatest possible scale: the Universe itself. In the box at left, **The very small meets the very large,** the incredibly minute and the unimaginably vast can be seen to meet at the top. By the end of this book, we shall indeed see how our understanding of the Universe on the largest scale rests upon our understanding of things on the smallest scale, and the same is true the other way round.

Towards infinity

We are all familiar with objects on a human scale, but gaining a feel for distances much larger than the size of the Earth can be difficult. The distance of the Earth from the Sun, for example, is already quite hard to grasp. It is about 150,000,000,000 metres (93 million miles); if you could fly to the Sun in a jet airliner the flight time would be more than twenty years – definitely not good for the circulation in your legs.

Working with such large numbers can be quite unwieldy and 150,000,000,000 is more usually written as 1.5×10^{11}, see **Speaking of size.** Moving out into the Universe introduces even greater quantities and astronomers use a much larger unit to measure length, based on the speed of light, which is 299,792,458 metres per second (about 186,280 miles per second). The distance light can travel in a certain time makes a convenient unit of length. It takes light about eight minutes to reach us from the Sun, so we say that the Sun is eight 'light-minutes' away. The furthest planet from the Sun, Pluto, is about six light-hours away, but it is the light-year that is most useful for expressing the enormous distances to objects outside our solar system. Since the light from the nearest star beyond the solar system, Proxima Centauri, takes four years to reach us, we say that it is four light-years away. This is about 38,000,000,000,000,000 or 3.8×10^{16} metres (733 million million miles).

On a larger scale, the Sun is one of about a hundred billion (a billion is a thousand million, 10^9) stars in a gigantic rotating disk called the Milky Way Galaxy, which is a hundred thousand light-years across. This means that light could have crossed it about 650 times since the dinosaurs became extinct.

On an even larger scale, space is studded with galaxies like the **Spiral galaxy M81** shown at top left. They are grouped into clusters, separated by vast empty regions. The nearest large galaxy outside our own is Andromeda, visible to the unaided eye on a very clear, dark night as a faint glow the size of the Moon. Andromeda is about two million light-years away and is a member of the Local Group, a small cluster of galaxies which includes the Milky Way. With a very powerful telescope, a vast number of galaxies can be observed, stretching out to such distances that the light coming from the very furthest would have been travelling for most of the time since the Universe was born. That was about 13.7 billion years ago and so they are more than 13.7 billion light-years away since the Universe is expanding. The furthest point in space that we can ever hope to see marks the limits of what is called the observable Universe, see **Ladder of cosmic scales.**

Powers of 10

1 000 000 000 000 000 000 000 000	10^{24}	yotta	Y
1 000 000 000 000 000 000 000	10^{21}	zetta	Z
1 000 000 000 000 000 000	10^{18}	exa	E
1 000 000 000 000 000	10^{15}	peta	P
1 000 000 000 000	10^{12}	tera	T
1 000 000 000	10^{9}	giga	G
1 000 000	10^{6}	mega	M
1 000	10^{3}	kilo	k
1	10^{0}		
0.001	10^{-3}	milli	m
0.000 001	10^{-6}	micro	μ
0.000 000 001	10^{-9}	nano	n
0.000 000 000 001	10^{-12}	pico	p
0.000 000 000 000 001	10^{-15}	femto	f
0.000 000 000 000 000 001	10^{-18}	atto	a
0.000 000 000 000 000 000 001	10^{-21}	zepto	z
0.000 000 000 000 000 000 000 001	10^{-24}	yocto	y

Speaking of size

The familiar 'kilometre' for thousand metres or 'millimetre', for a thousandth of a metre, do not help us much to talk about the really large or the very minute. This table presents the whole range of prefixes which apply not just to length (kilometre) but also to mass (kilogram) and other quantities.

Ladder of cosmic scales

The Earth is very close to the Sun compared to the distance from the Sun to the next star. The Sun and this star are, in turn, next door neighbours within the colossal extent of our Galaxy. Our Galaxy is almost lost within our local cluster of galaxies. All of these seem insignificant when compared to the immensity of the visible Universe.

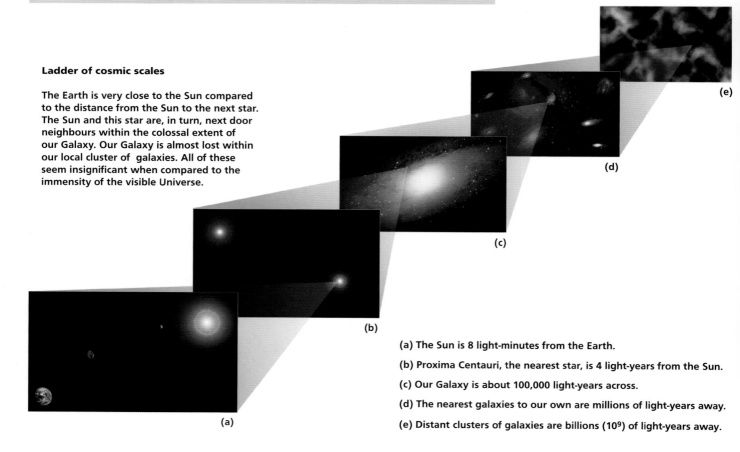

(a) The Sun is 8 light-minutes from the Earth.

(b) Proxima Centauri, the nearest star, is 4 light-years from the Sun.

(c) Our Galaxy is about 100,000 light-years across.

(d) The nearest galaxies to our own are millions of light-years away.

(e) Distant clusters of galaxies are billions (10^9) of light-years away.

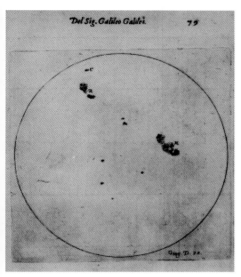

Sunspots

Galileo, using his telescope around 1610, took the first steps beyond what we can see with our eyes alone. This is his sketch of sunspots. (Royal Astronomical Society)

We cannot climb far up the cosmic ladder with the unaided eye. Galileo, see **Sunspots,** was the first to explore the heavens with a telescope. Half a century later, Robert Hooke, see **First glimpse of the microscopic**, took the first steps in exploring the world of the very small. We too will now set off into the world of the very small.

Under the microscope

The smallest unit of length with which most of us are familiar is the millimetre (a thousandth of a metre), but for the many objects that are only visible through a microscope, length scales are more sensibly expressed in terms of microns. A micron is a millionth of a metre, or a thousandth of a millimetre. A red blood cell, flowing with your blood, is about seven microns in diameter; and a typical bacterium is only one micron across. Viruses, which are responsible for many diseases including the common cold, can range in size from a few tenths down to a hundredth of a micron.

Small as viruses are, they are not the smallest of objects; they are, in common with everything else, structures made of atoms. Everything is composed of a few types of atoms arranged in an uncountable number of different ways, and an atom is only about one ten-thousandth the size of a micron. Thus there are about a billion atoms in a typical virus and a single glass of water contains more atoms than there are glasses of water in all the seas and oceans on Earth.

This book is about entities much smaller even than atoms. Each atom has a *nucleus* (plural *nuclei*) at its centre. A typical nucleus is about ten thousand times smaller than an atom — it is a tiny bundle of concentrated mass and energy, see **Further down the ladder**). The question of whether we have reached the limit of smallness with atomic nuclei is addressed later.

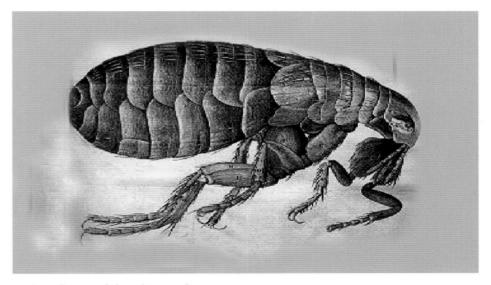

First glimpse of the microscopic

In the mid 17th century, Robert Hooke and Antoni van Leeuwenhoek explored the world of the very small. Their discoveries, like this flea drawn by Hooke, astonished their contemporaries.

It may seem surprising that we could learn much about things as tiny as atomic nuclei. Microscopes may have extended the range of our vision enormously, allowing us to see bacteria, but no ordinary light microscope will ever let us see a virus and they certainly will not work for atoms or nuclei. The reason for this is the nature of light.

Visible light is one form of **Electromagnetic radiation**, other forms being radio waves, infrared, ultraviolet, X-rays and gamma rays. Electromagnetic radiation travels as a wave; the different types vary according to their wavelength, which depends upon the amount of energy the radiation possesses, but they all travel in a vacuum at 'the speed of light'. It was not until the beginning of the nineteenth century that Thomas Young was able to prove that light travels in the form of waves. But waves of what? It was only towards the end of the nineteenth century that it was proved that they are waves of electric and magnetic fields; hence *electromagnetic* radiation.

The wavelength of visible light is about half a micron. Any object smaller than this, and any features smaller than this on an object, cannot be discerned using this type of electromagnetic radiation. That is why no optical microscope can distinguish objects smaller than the wavelength of the light shining on them, and why viruses were not seen until the 1940s. Their detection had to await the invention of a wholly new kind of microscope that did not use visible light.

The revolutionary new instrument, an **Electron microscope**, uses electron waves which have a much smaller wavelength. Electrons are the particles of electric charge that are present in every atom and which carry electric currents, but they can also behave as though they are waves. The wave character of electrons was the great discovery of a French prince **Louis duc de Broglie**. This discovery was a key step towards the understanding of the structure and properties of the subatomic world.

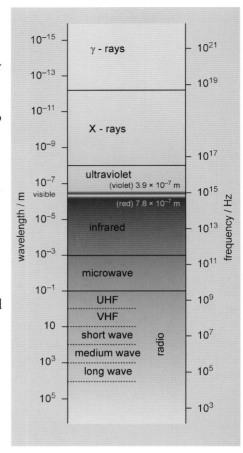

Electromagnetic radiation

Visible light has wavelengths between ultraviolet and infrared. It is just one form of electromagnetic radiation. All the other forms are fundamentally the same, differing only in wavelength (metres) and frequency (Hertz, or cycles per second).

Further down the ladder

(a) Within the atom, electrons exist as probability clouds that are represented here by fuzzy rings. The nucleus lies at the centre and has a radius 10,000 times smaller.

(b) It is made up of protons (red) and neutrons (blue).

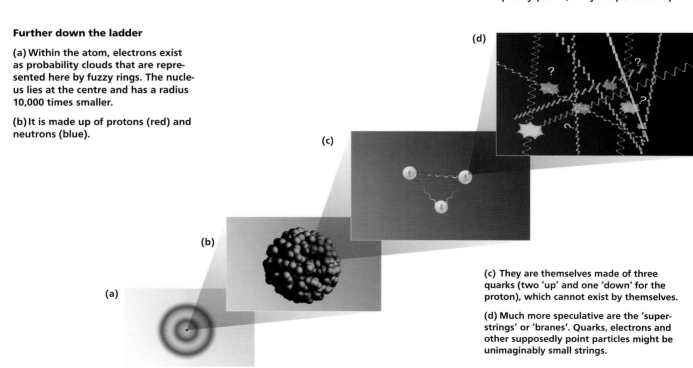

(c) They are themselves made of three quarks (two 'up' and one 'down' for the proton), which cannot exist by themselves.

(d) Much more speculative are the 'superstrings' or 'branes'. Quarks, electrons and other supposedly point particles might be unimaginably small strings.

Electron microscope

Here is a modern **electron** microscope flanked by an image of a human hair and, on the right and some 10,000 times smaller, a hepatitis B virus, showing its outer protein capsule which both protects it and provides the key which unlocks the defences of liver cells. (Courtesy LEO microscopes/John Berriman/MRC Cambridge.)

It sounds contradictory to describe electrons both as particles and as behaving like waves. This is the language of quantum mechanics, the physical theory in which electrons sometimes behave like waves and sometimes like particles. It is also the theory of the world of atoms and nuclei. For many purposes, electrons can be considered to be waves with a well-defined wavelength and this wavelength becomes shorter as the energy of the electrons is increased. Being waves, and also electrically charged, magnetic lenses can be made for beams of electrons and this allows the construction of electron microscopes. The shorter the electron wavelength, the finer the details of the object under study that can be seen. This is where electrons come into their own because they can be produced with much shorter wavelengths than ordinary light. The challenge is to produce electrons with the shortest possible wavelengths.

Increasing the energy of an electron reduces its quantum wavelength. An electron can be given a high energy by accelerating it in an electric field. Such a field exerts a force on any electrically charged particle, including an electron. Thus, electrons released into a vacuum will be accelerated if there is an electrical voltage across the vacuum. This is how electrons are accelerated in the cathode ray tubes that, until recently, were used in every television set and computer monitor. In these, the electrons (also known as 'cathode rays') are focused to a point that moves over the screen, tracing out the picture. In order to get the wavelength small enough to resolve the details of viruses, electron microscopes generally accelerate electrons to energies ten or more times higher than in a television cathode ray tube.

Atoms are much very much smaller than viruses. Today we understand how atoms are arranged in most materials, but as late as the first decade of the twentieth century many scientists doubted whether atoms even existed.

We now have a comprehensive theory, based on quantum mechanics, of how atoms arrange themselves into solids and liquids. But how can we possibly test these theories? Can we actually see how atoms are arranged in solids?

Louis Victor Pierre Raymond duc de Broglie, 1892–1987, the first person to glimpse the wave nature of matter. (Copyright the Nobel Foundation.)

Certainly, visible light could not help to establish how atoms are arranged in matter. Nowadays, however, we can obtain real images of atoms in the surface of a crystal, taken using a particular type of electron microscope called a scanning tunnelling microscope; for an example, see **Imaging sheets of atoms.** We shall see later that high-energy electrons are also valuable for measuring nuclei, but it is a non-visible form of electromagnetic radiation that has turned out to be the most significant source of information about the structure of matter: X-rays.

X-rays have wavelengths typically a thousand times smaller than visible light. Unfortunately it is not possible to build X-ray microscopes because there is no suitable system of lenses that can bring X-rays to a focus within such an instrument. Nevertheless, not long after they were discovered, X-rays were used to study the structure of matter. The secret is to use a universal property of all waves: *diffraction*.

Early in the nineteenth century, **Thomas Young** demonstrated how visible light falling upon a pair of slits, leads to a pattern of light and dark regions, a *diffraction pattern*. Such a pattern is shown in the **Double-slit diffraction pattern of light.**

How such a pattern is formed is shown with water waves in **How waves diffract.** Knowing the wavelength of the light and the spacing of the slits, it is possible to work out the details of the diffraction pattern. In the same way, more complicated patterns of holes, forming a so-called 'grating', lead to more complicated patterns of light and dark. Working backwards from particular complicated diffraction patterns it is possible to determine what sort of 'grating' gave rise to those patterns.

The breakthrough came when it was realized by von Laue and by W. H. Bragg and his son W. L. Bragg, that the atoms arranged in an orderly way in a crystal are, in effect, a diffraction grating. For example, the diffraction of X-rays by a crystal of common salt gives a measurement of the distance between the sodium and chlorine atoms in such crystals, see **A salt crystal.** Much more interesting crystals than common salt have been studied with X-rays: it was by looking at the way X-rays were diffracted by DNA that Francis Crick and James Watson unravelled the double helix structure of this key molecule of life in Cambridge in 1953.

Imaging sheets of atoms

This is the surface of a crystal of iron silicide as seen using a device called a scanning tunnelling microscope. The smallest step corresponds to a layer one atom thick. (Courtesy Nanoscale Science Laboratory, Cambridge.)

Thomas Young, 1773–1829, polymath. It was Young who first provided convincing evidence of the wave nature of light. (AIP Emilio Segrè Visual Archives)

How waves diffract

When light falls on a barrier with tiny holes or slits in it, a pattern of light and dark can be found on a screen placed on the far side. The same sort of thing happens with any waves, including water waves where it is easier to see what is happening.

Waves spread out when they encounter objects, something most easily observed when their wavelength is comparable to the size of the object. This spreading out is known as diffraction. Waves from different holes interfere with each other and where a trough arriving from one hole meets a crest from another they can cancel each other out. For light waves this means there are dark patches at such places, as Thomas Young discovered.

We can also go much deeper into the structure of matter and discern much finer details than the structure of crystals. To do this we must find waves with even shorter wavelengths than those of X-rays; these are the waves that de Broglie showed belong to high-energy electrons. Such electrons are not only used in electron microscopes to study viruses, for example, but *much* higher energies and *much* shorter wavelengths are possible. This opens the door to studying objects *much* smaller than viruses: the diffraction of high-energy electrons allows us to study the size and shape of atomic nuclei.

So now we leave the realm of atoms for the realm of nuclei, ten thousand times smaller. When X-rays were first used to study crystals, there was no reason to suspect that Nature had structures on such a small scale. Clues of this 'sub'-atomic world came in the shape of a wholly unexpected new phenomenon: radioactivity.

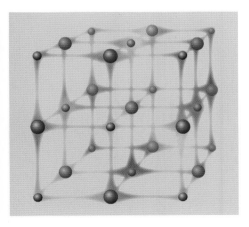

A salt crystal

A crystal of common salt consists of alternating sodium and chlorine atoms arranged in a regular cubic array. The spacing between the atoms can be worked out from the way X-rays diffract from the crystal.

Double-slit diffraction pattern of light

The interference pattern from two slits demonstrates the wave-like propagation of light.

2. The discovery of nuclei

How a new world was revealed by radioactivity

As the nineteenth century drew to a close, many scientists felt that all the important questions in science had been answered. This was wishful thinking. Scientists could not even agree that matter was made of atoms let alone explain something as basic as why copper is red! The majority just thought that it was because copper had 'redness'. Today, such a statement would not be acceptable; the colour of copper can be explained with far more convincing arguments, but only because the structure of atoms is understood more thoroughly. But how could we study the structure of atoms, things that were so small that many doubted whether they existed?

Our story of how we became able to investigate atoms begins with a complete scientific surprise. In 1895 **Wilhelm Röntgen** astonished the world with his discovery of **X-rays**. He had been investigating the source that had fogged some photographic plates in his laboratory. These plates had been kept carefully wrapped to keep out the light. Röntgen eventually tracked down the fogging to some invisible rays coming from a gas-discharge tube. The discovery of X-rays sent shock waves around the world. Here were mysterious new rays that could pass through solid materials to cloud photographic film. Very soon, people all over the world were marvelling at photographs showing the **Bones** in their hands.

The mysterious X-rays seemed to be streaming out of a part of the tube that glowed in the dark; it was fluorescent. This property caught the attention of **Henri Becquerel** in Paris. Becquerel studied a uranium compound that he knew also emitted such an eerie glow. He found, just like X-rays, that the radiation from uranium could pass through the black paper protecting photographic film from light, and leave its traces on the undeveloped film; see **New rays make their mark**. Unlike X-rays, which disappeared when the X-ray tube

Wilhelm Röntgen, 1845–1923, whose accidental discovery of X-rays in 1895 opened a new window on the world. (Copyright the Nobel Foundation.)

Bones

X-rays came into their own during the first world war. This image of a hand with a shell splinter is taken from Marie Curie's book "Radiology in War", published in 1921. (ACJC-Archives Curie and Joliot-Curie.)

X-rays

X-rays stimulated scientists around the world into action. They also aroused a great deal of public interest which had not abated decades later, as the cigarette card shows.

Henri Bequerel, 1852–1908, won the Nobel Prize for Physics in 1903 with Marie and Pierre Curie. (Copyright the Nobel Foundation.)

was switched off, the radiation from the uranium compound was emitted continuously. Becquerel soon found that *any* compound of uranium, even pure uranium metal, worked just as well.

For a while, X-rays were the focus of the excitement, and few recognized the deep significance of Becquerel's discovery, which took some time to be recognized. After all, the discovery of X-rays had very obvious applications in medicine and industry, as well as raising many scientific questions. X-rays also gripped the public imagination with popular cartoons making jokes about how the new rays would penetrate the many layers of Victorian petticoats.

The hunt for radioactive elements

Marie Curie in Paris was one of the few scientists of the time who was inspired to continue Becquerel's work After all, only uranium and its compounds were known to emit these new rays. But Marie Curie had the instinct of a great scientist to spot a wholly new window into nature and she soon found that another element, thorium, had the same property as uranium. Until the 1890s, thorium was just an element whose oxide was used to make gas lighting mantles bright, while uranium had been used since Roman times as a yellow pigment in glass. These rather boring elements were about to leap to the centre of the scientific stage and offer unique clues about the structure of matter.

Just as for uranium, the chemical form of thorium did not matter. All forms – thorium metal, thorium oxide etc. – emitted exactly the same rays, which, just as for uranium, poured out steadily without any external source of energy being applied. It was Marie Curie who first used the word 'radioactivity' to describe the radiation emitted by uranium and thorium. Born Marie Sklodowska, she had recently arrived in Paris from Poland and married Pierre Curie, who had himself already made some important discoveries in physics, see **The Curies**. The story of how Marie Curie discovered polonium, a new radioactive element lurking in trace amounts in uranium ore, followed by radium, an element far more radioactive than uranium and very much rarer, is an inspiring one.

Unlike uranium, pure radium glows in the dark. It also gives out heat. Even the tiny amounts that Marie Curie was able to extract radiated a measurable supply of heat. Radium soon became highly prized as a source of powerful radiation for further experiments. From the earliest days, it was also studied as a possible cure for cancer. This was the beginning of radiotherapy.

New X-rays make their mark

The faint image of a Maltese Cross shows where some of the radiation was absorbed by metal in the shape of a Maltese Cross. The photographic film was shielded from the light with paper. This image was made by Henri Becquerel.

Rutherford joins the quest

Meanwhile, a young New Zealander called **Ernest Rutherford** had arrived in Britain to work in Cambridge with **J. J. Thomson**, one of the greatest experimental physicist of the day. 'J. J.' was interested in how X-rays made air conduct electricity. If you rub a plastic ruler on a woollen sweater, it will pick up small pieces of paper. This is because it acquires an electric charge on its surface. Near an X-ray machine, such a ruler quickly loses its charge because the air becomes conducting and the charge drains away. The reason for this is that the X-rays ionize the air by freeing some electric charge (electrons) from their atoms.

Thomson and Rutherford initially set out to explore this ionization by X-rays. It was known that Becquerel's new kind of radiation also ionized air and exploring this new phenomenon of radioactivity soon became Rutherford's passion. At about this time, temporarily leaving his work on X-rays, Thomson made the momentous discovery that electric charge exists in packets or particles of electricity, now called electrons, see box **The discovery of the electron**. For this, he won the Nobel Prize. It is now known that electric currents in wires are just the flow of electrons; and electrons are a key component of every atom.

Shaking the foundations of science

While Thomson worked on the nature of electric charge, Rutherford made his first big breakthrough. He found that there were two distinct kinds of radioactivity. This was not a trivial discovery in the days before modern instruments; it had the hallmarks of insight and ingenuity that were to make Rutherford famous.

Joseph John Thomson, 1856–1940, discoverer of the electron, the first fundamental particle of Nature to be identified. In 1906 he was awarded the Nobel prize in physics. (Copyright the Nobel Foundation.)

The Curies

Pierre, 1859–1906, and Marie Curie, 1867–1934, in their laboratory in 1898. (ACJC-Archives Curie and Joliot-Curie.)

He discovered that one kind of radiation was highly ionizing and very easily absorbed, even by thin sheets of paper. He called this 'alpha' radiation. The other type was far more penetrating and was named 'beta' radiation. Eventually gamma rays were discovered too, see **Three kinds of radiation**.

Soon afterwards, Rutherford established one of the most puzzling and characteristic features of radioactivity: no matter how much radioactive material is present initially, half of it will disappear after a time interval known as the 'half-life'. After two half-lives, only a quarter of the original material remains, and so on. This property, known as exponential decay, is tied up with the quantum mechanical nature of atoms described in the next chapter. Rutherford followed these findings with another important discovery that earned him, somewhat to his amusement, the Nobel Prize in chemistry in 1908.

The discovery of the electron

J. J. Thomson discovered the electron with this apparatus, a forerunner of the cathode ray tube, which, until the advent of the flat screen, was found in computer monitors and TV sets. Rays emitted from the 'cathode', C, strike the fluorescent screen at the far end of the tube, leaving a spot of light. Thomson's genius was to interpret the paths of the rays in terms of charged corpuscles, later called electrons. Electrodes A and B were at a positive voltage, drawing off the electrons through the slits. These were then bent by electric and magnetic fields. Electrodes D and E supplied the electric fields, external coils provided the magnetic fields.

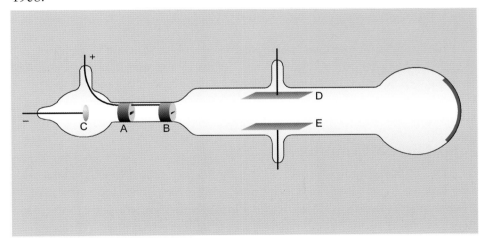

Three kinds of radiation

Alpha (α) particles are stopped by a thin sheet of paper but beta and gamma rays pass through. Beta (β) rays are stopped by a thin aluminium foil, but gamma (γ) rays easily pass. Gamma rays can pass through several centimetres of lead.

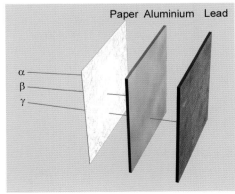

The end of chemistry's most cherished belief

Elements are the foundation stones of chemistry. The vast variety of substances around us are made from combining elements – such as carbon, oxygen, hydrogen and nitrogen – in different ways. At the turn of the twentieth century, a firmly held belief was that atoms never change. Carbon atoms remain carbon atoms; iron stays iron; gold cannot be made from lead; and once uranium, always uranium. Rutherford and his colleague **Frederick Soddy**, who was at that time working with him at McGill University in Montreal, Canada, overturned this idea. They found radioactivity was a process that could transform one element into another. Somehow, one type of atom emitted a particle and became another type of atom. No doubt mindful of the ill-repute arising from thousands of years of futile attempts to make gold from lead, Rutherford is reported to have said : "Don't call it transmutation, Soddy, or they'll have our heads as alchemists!" The idea of atoms transmuting from one type to another met with initial resistance, even from the Curies. Within a few years, however, such overwhelming evidence was presented by Rutherford, Soddy and many others, that transmutation became widely accepted. A great number of people were soon involved in unravelling the complicated story of which element transmuted into what. This task was made much easier by knowing the nature of alpha and beta radiation, as well as by the discovery of a third type of radioactivity called gamma rays.

Frederick Soddy, 1877-1956. As well as contributing to the discovery of transmutation, he was the first to identify the concept of 'isotope', for which he gained the Nobel prize in chemistry for 1921. (Copyright the Nobel Foundation.)

The nature of radiation

Following the discovery of alpha and beta radiation, physicists were keen to investigate their nature. Beta particles were relatively easy to identify. Their paths are deflected easily by strong magnets, which shows that they are electrically charged and are thousands of times lighter than atoms. Beta particles were soon identified as electrons – the particles recently discovered by Thomson to be the smallest carriers of electric charge.

The nature of alpha particles was harder to establish. They are certainly electrically charged, but are much harder to deflect by magnets, which means that they have to be much heavier than electrons. Rutherford discovered that alpha particles are helium ions, in other words, helium atoms that have been stripped of their electrons, leaving them positively charged.

Age of the Earth mystery

The idea of transmutation, together with an understanding of what alpha and beta rays are, opened up the possibility of using radioactivity for a variety of measurements. By 1905, Rutherford could claim to know the age of the rocks he was carrying in his pocket simply because he knew that alpha particles were helium ions.

Rocks naturally contain a small amount of radioactive uranium that transforms into another element, spitting out helium ions in the process. The helium ions soon pick up their missing electrons and become neutral helium atoms, which are trapped in the rocks. These minerals are studied in a laboratory to see how much helium they hold.

Knowing the amount of helium locked away in the rocks, Rutherford could determine how much time had passed since the rocks were formed. He had to take into account the amount of uranium in the rock along with other elements, such as lead, which are the end products of a whole chain of transmutations starting with uranium. Today, analyses like this are crucial to geology, and dating rocks by studying the decay of radioactive minerals is a highly developed application of nuclear techniques, which we say more about in Chapter 7.

Having demolished one of chemistry's most cherished beliefs – namely that the elements cannot change from one type to another – radioactivity was also beginning to threaten a cornerstone of physics. This was the law proclaiming that energy is always conserved. Although it can be transformed from one form to another, the total amount of energy of a system always remains the same. How could radioactive materials seemingly pour out energy from nowhere? This was a real dilemma. Later it was found that the total mass of nuclear particles becomes less following radioactive decay. It was Albert Einstein who first showed that a loss of mass means a release of energy.

But in 1904, before Einstein's theory of relativity, nuclear energy solved another vexing problem. The great physicist Lord Kelvin had estimated that the Earth could not be more than 100 million years old, otherwise its interior would have had time to cool down. Geologists argued that it was much older; and biologists knew that life would have needed much more time to evolve. Rutherford pointed out that the radioactivity of minerals in the ground was an additional source of heat, which made a much older Earth possible. In fact, the rocks in his pocket were themselves much older than Kelvin's estimate of the **Age of the Earth**.

The next application of radioactivity was momentous: studying the inner structure of matter itself. Rutherford realized that radioactivity might tell us something even more fundamental than the age of the Earth: the result was the discovery of the atomic nucleus.

Signatures of the invisible

In spite of the unimaginably small size of each alpha particle – about a million, million times smaller than a flea – individual alpha particles can be detected. This remarkable fact made it possible to use radioactivity to explore the fundamental structure of all matter.

A single alpha particle striking a screen made of zinc sulphide creates a tiny flash of light (a scintillation). The ability to see these flashes attests to the extreme sensitivity of human eyes to tiny amounts of light – sensitivity, that is, only for people prepared to spend hours in a pitch-dark room allowing their eyes to adapt. This was a price the early explorers of radioactivity were happy to pay. Even the fact that the flashes occurred at all was significant, since the fact that there were individual flashes was one of the clinching arguments persuading some scientists of the very existence of atoms.

By the first decade of the twentieth century, there were various 'informed' guesses as to the structure of atoms. The most widely known of these was Thomson's 'plum pudding' model. According to Thomson, the negatively charged electrons were dotted like plums in a pudding made of positively charged matter. Although he did not know how many 'plums' the pudding contained, there had to be enough electrons to make the positive and negative charges balance as, overall, atoms are electrically neutral. A key point of

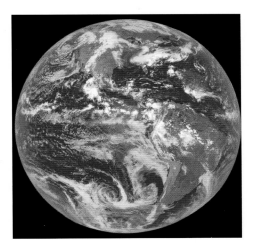

Age of the Earth

Our blue planet is approximately 4.5 billion years old. If it were not for the nuclear decay processes at the core, the Earth would have cooled down to a solid ball long ago, without plate tectonics, earthquakes or volcanoes. This is discussed further in Chapter 7. (Courtesy of M. Jentoft-Nilsen, F. Hasler, D. Chesters NASA/Goddard and T. Nielsen University of Hawaii.)

Thomson's model was that the positive charge was spread throughout the atom, rather than concentrated at a particular point. Thomson and his contemporaries never expected that such a model could ever be tested – atoms were then far beyond the power of any imaginable microscope – and as for seeing their internal structure, that was just a dream.

Discovery of the nucleus

Rutherford moved to Manchester, England, in 1907 where he carried out experiments with alpha particles in meticulous detail, see **Geiger and Rutherford in Manchester**. One feature struck him as very puzzling: as they passed through air or thin sheets of mica the paths of the alpha particles seemed to deviate very slightly from straight lines. Whereas lesser mortals might have shrugged it off, Rutherford spotted a real problem because alpha particles passing through an atom like that of Thomson's plum pudding model would hardly be deflected at all. Rutherford enlisted the help of Ernest Marsden, an undergraduate student who was being trained by his colleague Hans Geiger, who was working with Rutherford at the time. In Rutherford's words: "One day Geiger came to me and said, 'Don't you think that young Marsden, whom I am training in radioactive methods, ought to begin a small research?' Now I had thought so too, so I said, 'Why not let him see if any alpha particles can be scattered through a large angle?'"

As this research occurred before the development of the Geiger counter, Geiger and Marsden had to physically count the individual scintillations, viewed under a microscope as the alpha particles hit a zinc sulphide screen. Using this technique, they measured the fraction of alpha particles that were

Geiger and Rutherford in Manchester

Hans Geiger, 1882–1947, left, with Ernest Rutherford, 1871–1937, in Rutherford's laboratory in Manchester. This picture was taken at about the time of the discovery of the nucleus. (Science Museum/Science and Society Picture Library.)

deflected by the atoms in a thin sheet of gold placed between the radioactive source and the screen.

Most of the alpha particles went almost straight through, deflected only slightly by the gold foil, while a small but significant number of alpha particles were scattered at large angles. You can see this in the box, **Result of the measurements** where you will see that the number of particles deflected through 120 degrees is about 10^4 times less than deflected through 20 degrees. This prompted Rutherford to exclaim: "It was as though you had fired a fifteen inch shell at a piece of tissue paper and it had bounced back and hit you." Rutherford knew that the positive electrical charge was just too spread out in the plum-pudding model to provide the huge force needed to turn the alpha particles round in their tracks. After all, the alpha particles were moving at a good fraction of the speed of light. The only way to muster sufficient force would be if most of each atom's mass and electric charge were concentrated in a tiny volume. Certainly, the alpha particles could not bounce back from the electrons, which are 8000 time less massive – that would be like a grain of rice deflecting a bowling ball.

Rutherford deduced that the alpha particles must be scattered by a very small, dense, charged nucleus at the centre of the atom. If the positive charge were spread evenly throughout the volume of each atom, all the alpha particles would have gone through the target virtually undeflected.

Scattering unlocks the secrets

Geiger and Marsden's simple first experiment with gold atoms was a slender foundation for a revolutionary new picture of matter. Something more detailed was required, and that was soon forthcoming. From his nuclear model of the atom, Rutherford calculated how many particles should be scattered at what angles for different types of material. To do this he made use of the latest ideas from chemistry, which predicted how much electric charge the nuclei of atoms of aluminium, silver and gold might have.

Geiger and Marsden bombarded a whole range of substances with alpha particles. To see how they did it, look at the box on the next page **Scattering alpha particles.** Counting individual zinc sulphide scintillations in the dark using a microscope, they then painstakingly measured what proportion of the particles went straight through various thin metal foils, what proportion were bounced back and the numbers scattered at all the intermediate angles. Extreme patience was needed to get a reasonable number of counts for the large angles to make the results meaningful. Rutherford freely admitted that he did not have the patience for the job.

Geiger and Marsden's measurements matched Rutherford's predictions perfectly as you can see in the box **Result of the meaurements**. These pioneers with their acute eyes and patience were rewarded with the confirmation of a momentous discovery: atoms have nuclei. Their discovery revolutionized not just physics, but also astronomy, chemistry, biology and our everyday view of the world. The experiments even made it possible to say that the hydrogen and helium nuclei must be less than four femtometres in diameter (a fem-

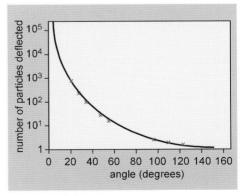

Result of the measurements

The solid line shows Rutherford's prediction that many alpha particles would be scattered through small angles, but much fewer at large angles. The dots show the measurements of Geiger and Marsden agreeing very well. According to pre-nuclear models, all alpha particles would hardly be deflected at all.

tometre being 4×10^{-15} of a metre) and that the gold nucleus must be no more than ten times this size. To put these numbers into perspective, one femtometre is to one micron what a micron is to a kilometre. Or to put it another way, the size of a typical nucleus relative to one metre is about the same as the size of a pinhead relative to the distance between the Earth and the Sun. See **A solar system analogy.**

These experiments did much more than prove the existence of atomic nuclei. They inaugurated a whole new method of studying nature: the scattering experiment. Even today, the most important way to study atoms and their nuclei is to fire a beam of particles at a target and watch how they are scattered. It is certainly not at all obvious that we could ever learn anything about atoms that are 10^{-10} metres across, or nuclei that are between 10,000 to 100,000 times smaller still, but, nearly a hundred years later, we have learnt a huge amount, mostly from scattering experiments. Today, such experiments are vastly more complex than Geiger and Marsden's, but they are based on the same principle. Particle accelerators can provide particles at far higher energies and intensities than radioactive sources, and scientists no longer sit in darkened rooms counting flashes of light with their eyes. Instead they use complex electronic detectors and an array of computers to sort and store many gigabytes of data from the experiments. The LHC at CERN is simply the latest in a long line of more and more sophisticated ways of understanding the structure of matter by means of scattering particles of higher and higher energy.

Rutherford knew that his nuclear model left many unresolved problems. For example, if all the positive charge were in the tiny central nucleus, while the negatively charged electrons orbited around like planets around the Sun, why did these electrons, which are attracted to the positive charge, simply not fall into the nucleus and neutralize it? There is an important difference between an atom and the Solar System. The Earth and other planets are all in stable orbits around the Sun, whereas the orbiting electrons should be losing energy as they go round the nucleus. This is because electric charges emit radiation when they are accelerated; a particle moving in circular motion is accelerating towards the central point, even if its speed is constant. This loss of energy by

Scattering alpha particles

The apparatus used by Geiger and Marsden to verify Rutherford's prediction of alpha particle scattering. R is the alpha emitter, F is the foil, S is the fluorescent screen and M is the viewing microscope. Screen and microscope could be moved around so that the number of alpha particles scattered at different angles could be counted. The detector is at a small scattering angle above and at a large scattering angle below.

A Solar System analogy

The Solar System is a nice analogy for the strong deflection of alpha particles passing through an atom. A comet's path is very curved close to the Sun. This is because the Sun's gravitational force is large near the Sun and much smaller further away. If the mass of the Sun were spread through the huge volume of the Solar System, a body coming from outside the Solar System would only be weakly deflected. In the same way, an alpha particle would be weakly deflected if the positive charge were not concentrated in a tiny volume, the nucleus. (Julian Baum)

RADIATION AND ABSORPTION SPECTRA.

[For description, see back.

Atomic fingerprints

Each element has a unique light 'fingerprint' or spectrum. The different colours emitted when the element is heated can be separated by passing the light through a prism or other kind of 'spectroscope'. The resulting pattern is called an emission spectrum. If white light, composed of all colours, passes through a vapour containing atoms of a particular element, then those atoms all absorb light of the same colours. The result is called an absorption spectrum and can be seen as a series of black lines shown here. This picture, showing a range of different spectra, was the frontispiece of Norman Lockyer's "Elementary Lessons in Astronomy" 1874. Lockyer became famous for discovering helium on the Sun before it was known on Earth – and it is also for this reason that the element was named after the Greek word for the Sun, 'Helios'.

| 656.210 nm | | 486.074 nm | 434.010 nm | 410.12 nm |

Balmer series

Each of these four lines in the visible spectrum of hydrogen corresponds to a specific amount of energy emitted by hydrogen atoms. These energies are the 'quantum leaps' which occur when the hydrogen atom drops from one of its possible energies to a lower energy.

radiation means that the electrons should rapidly spiral in towards the nucleus. The resolution of this puzzle would require a stroke of genius from a young newcomer.

Electrons in orbit

A young Dane called Niels Bohr was on an extended visit to Rutherford in Manchester. Bohr's answer to Rutherford's problem also explained a puzzling property of the light given out when an electric current is passed through hydrogen gas. All elements have a particular pattern of colours, see **Atomic fingerprints**. A Swiss schoolteacher, Johann Balmer, had earlier discovered a remarkable mathematical pattern when analysing the colour of the light from Hydrogen. Scientists believed that a strikingly regular pattern like the so-called '**Balmer series**' should have a clear-cut explanation. The spectra of the other elements shown in Atomic fingerprints are much more complicated than that of hydrogen, the simplest element.

Bohr solved the mystery of why electrons don't fall into the nuclei and, at the same time, explained the Balmer series with a brilliant modification of Rutherford's model. The basic idea was that the electrons do not fall into the nucleus because, as they revolve around the nucleus, they are confined to a series of fixed orbits. In such an orbit they do not radiate energy. It was almost as if there were a number of invisible rail-tracks around the nucleus on which the electrons had to run, see **Bohr's models**. The electrons can, however, radiate when they jump from one orbit to another. These orbits were determined by the standard theories of physics of Bohr's day, with the crucial addition of a new ingredient: the quantum theory of Max Planck and Albert Einstein. The different spectral lines of the Balmer series just correspond to the different possible jumps the electron can make between the allowed orbits of the hydrogen atom. So, instead of the electrons continuously spiraling inwards, they jump from orbit to orbit until they reach the orbit having the lowest energy. With each jump, light of a specific frequency is emitted, carrying off energy. When the electron reaches the orbit having the lowest energy, it will radiate no more. The hydrogen atom is said to be in its ground state. This state is reached by any isolated hydrogen atom.

Planck and Einstein had used the revolutionary idea that energy comes in packets called 'quanta' to explain a number of puzzling properties of radiation and heat. In 1913, Bohr applied these ideas to atoms and gave a first explanation of why electrons in atoms did not fall into the nuclei. His model convinced many people of Rutherford's nuclear picture of the atom, and was a key step towards the quantum theory that was later to become the basic theory of all phenomena at the atomic scale.

Bohr's models

Bohr's model of hydrogen (top left). Later he developed models for Helium (top right) and neon atoms (below).

That was far from the end of the story. While most people were convinced that there must be something to Bohr's model, it failed to account for many of the properties of atoms other than hydrogen. It was not until the rise of quantum mechanics in the 1920s that the full picture of atomic structure emerged.

Ingredients to make an element

Despite its limitations, the broad concept of Bohr's atomic model remains applicable today. It furnishes a framework for understanding the chemical elements and also provides the language used to describe atoms and nuclei. The total charge on a neutral atom is zero because the negative charge on all the electrons balances the positive charge on the nucleus; the number of electrons in an atom equals the number of positively charged particles in the nucleus. This quantity is called the atomic number and is denoted by the letter Z. The Z of a particular atom tells us which chemical element it is. For example, the simplest element, hydrogen, has $Z=1$, while the next simplest element, helium, has $Z=2$. Helium therefore has two electrons in orbit about a compact nucleus containing two positive charges.

Hydrogen and helium are the most abundant elements in the Universe. About three-quarters of the matter in the Universe is hydrogen and the rest is mostly helium. The other 90 or so elements make up the remaining 2%. Of course, there are certain places where some of these elements, like carbon, oxygen and iron, are more common. The Earth is one such place. Except for hydrogen, helium and lithium, the chemical elements are all made in stars. For example, gold is made when a massive star explodes as a supernova, while lead is mostly made in 'red giant' stars and thrown off into space, perhaps to end up in the plumbing of a planet like ours. There will be more about how elements are made in stars in Chapter 9.

Protons, neutrons and isotopes

Rutherford gave the hydrogen nucleus a name of its own: the proton. The electric charge of the proton is equal and opposite to that of the electron and it weighs about 2000 times more, consistent with Rutherford's model of the atom having most of its mass in the central nucleus.

The helium nucleus is four times heavier than the hydrogen nucleus, not twice as massive as might be expected. This is because it contains two uncharged particles called neutrons, as well as the two protons. Protons and neutrons have about the same mass. In fact, not all hydrogen nuclei consist of just a lone proton: some also contain one or two neutrons. Similarly, not all helium nuclei are made of two protons and two neutrons, a few have two protons but only one neutron. Nuclei with a particular number of protons can have different numbers of neutrons. However, it is the number of protons that identifies a particular element, not the number of neutrons. Atoms with different numbers of neutrons but the same number of protons (and electrons) are different *isotopes* of the same element. It is the atomic number Z that determines essentially all of the chemical properties that are characteristic of a particular element. The general term nucleon is often used to refer to a proton or a neutron: thus, helium nuclei contain 4 nucleons.

Each element has a number of different isotopes. In fact, nuclei are usually identified by a third number, called the atomic mass number A, which refers to the total number of protons and neutrons. For example, most of the carbon atoms in the world have 6 protons and 6 neutrons, giving them an atomic mass number $A = 12$. These are the atoms of the isotope sometimes written as carbon-12. Henceforth, we will use the nuclear physics convention of writing this as ^{12}C, where the letter denotes the chemical symbol of the element. An isotope of carbon with 8 neutrons also exists in small quantities. These rarer ^{14}C atoms are radioactive and can be used to date ancient remains, a technique known as 'carbon dating'.

There exist many more radioactive (unstable) isotopes than stable isotopes. The element with the largest number of stable isotopes is tin, Sn, with $Z = 50$. The stable isotopes of tin have $A = 112, 114, 115, 116, 117, 118, 119, 120, 122,$ and 124, denoted ^{112}Sn, etc. You might notice two things: one is that they all the stable isotopes of tin have more neutrons than protons ($A = 112$ has 62 neutrons since $50 + 62 = 112$). The other is that the odd numbers 113, 121 and 123, are missing. It turns out that virtually all nuclei have more neutrons than protons and, moreover, there is a strong preference for even numbers of protons and neutrons. These facts demand explanation, and this will be given in Chapter 6.

We can now say exactly what an alpha particle is. It is the nucleus of the most common isotope of helium: ^{4}He. The reason why some heavier nuclei choose to emit such objects is part of the unfolding drama, as we continue our journey into the heart of matter.

Nuclear notation

A nucleus is denoted by the chemical symbol of its element along with a number denoting the sum of the number of protons and neutrons it contains. Thus ^{12}C (you read it as carbon-twelve) is a nucleus with 6 protons (the signature of carbon) and 6 neutrons whereas the isotope ^{14}C, which also contains 6 protons, has two extra neutrons. Atomic and nuclear masses are often given in atomic mass units (amu), where one amu (or 1.66×10^{-27} kg) is defined as one twelfth of the mass of the neutral ^{12}C atom. The total number of nucleons is known as the atomic mass number, or just mass number.

Some important Isotopes

Symbol	Nucleus
^{1}H	ordinary hydrogen
^{2}H	deuterium (heavy hydrogen)
^{3}H	tritium (radioactive hydrogen)
^{4}He	helium (alpha particle)
^{12}C	carbon, commonest isotope
^{14}C	rare radioactive isotope, used for dating
^{16}O	oxygen, common isotope
^{56}Fe	iron, common isotope
^{235}U	uranium, rare isotope
^{238}U	uranium, most common isotope

3. Particles or waves?

Strange laws at the heart of matter

Television news items or films sometimes show someone using a Geiger counter… maybe a prospector is searching for uranium, or perhaps a hospital worker is accounting for vital radioactive materials used to treat cancer. Geiger counters are particle detectors that make a characteristic clicking sound every time a high energy particle enters. Click – one particle; click – another particle.

It is known that X-rays are emitted by electrons in the atom, whereas gamma rays, electromagnetic radiation of an even higher energy, are emitted from within the atomic nucleus. The clicking of a Geiger counter is a sign of quantum weirdness – the gamma ray waves are behaving as particles. In the same way that particles like electrons can sometimes behave as waves (we have mentioned how the wave properties of electrons allow us to study the structure of matter), all electromagnetic waves can occasionally act as particles.

Every type of particle has a name, and particles of light are called photons. All electromagnetic waves, whether they are gamma rays, X-rays, visible, ultraviolet light, or radio waves, consist of photons. These forms of electromagnetic radiation differ in the frequency of their oscillations in a way that can be seen in **Electromagnetic radiation** on page 18.

An important property of electromagnetic waves is that, unlike other forms of waves such as sound, they do not need a medium to carry them. Sound waves require air or some other material to travel through, but all forms of light can propagate through empty space. It is because photons happily travel in the near vacuum of space that the radiation emitted by the Sun gives warmth and light to the Earth.

J. L. Cassingham with one of his company's Geiger counters, featured in an advertisement from 1955. (Courtesy J. L. and Curtis Cassingham.)

The strange world of photons

Every day, photons of visible light enable us to find our way about and to enjoy our environment. We can extend our visual sense with microscopes to study objects that would otherwise be too small to see with the naked eye. But ordinary microscopes are no help when it comes to discerning structures smaller than the wavelength of visible light. To see the details of such structures we need to use photons with shorter wavelengths. Investigating the diffraction patterns caused by shining X-rays through salt crystals, for example, allows the spacing between the atoms to be measured. The process by which the diffraction pattern is created can be understood in terms of quantum effects as follows.

Imagine turning down the intensity of the X-ray beam until just one photon passes through the crystal at a time. A single photon like this can act like a particle, blackening a single minute grain of sensitive material on a photographic film. However, if we fire a huge number of photons one at a time at the crystal, aiming exactly the same way each time, then the spots eventually build up into a diffraction pattern of the sort we associate with waves.

While each photon arrives at the film as a tiny particle, the only way the diffraction pattern could build up is for each photon to 'see' the whole array of ions. Somehow, like a wave, it must pass through the whole crystal and yet, like a particle, it will blacken a single grain on a photographic film. A single minute spot on a film is not a diffraction pattern; only after a huge number of individual photons have passed through the crystal does the pattern build up.

Weird quantum effects

In our X-ray shoot-out, the photons do not pile up at the same spot on the film even though they were aimed and fired in exactly the same way. The pattern that builds up reveals the wave nature of the particles as more and more photons hit the film. It is impossible to predict where any particular photon will turn up on the film, yet the overall pattern that eventually builds up consists of groups of spots clustered together in bands with gaps in between where there are no spots. This diffraction pattern is a feature that always shows up whenever quantum effects are important.

Many people find this 'uncertainty' one of the most disconcerting characteristics of quantum behaviour. For centuries, science has been based on the idea that a particular situation always leads to the same outcome. In the X-ray diffraction experiment, this rule is broken: it is simply impossible to predict where a photon will leave its mark on the film.

All is not lost, however. A new, but limited, kind of predictability emerges from the ruins of the old predictability, in which people believed they could say where a particle would go. The pattern that builds up from a large number of unpredictable spots is itself predictable, and can be reproduced whenever the entire experiment is repeated. We just have to abandon the idea that we can ever say where an individual photon will blacken the film. This strange new interplay of predictability and unpredictability turns up repeatedly in the realm of atomic nuclei.

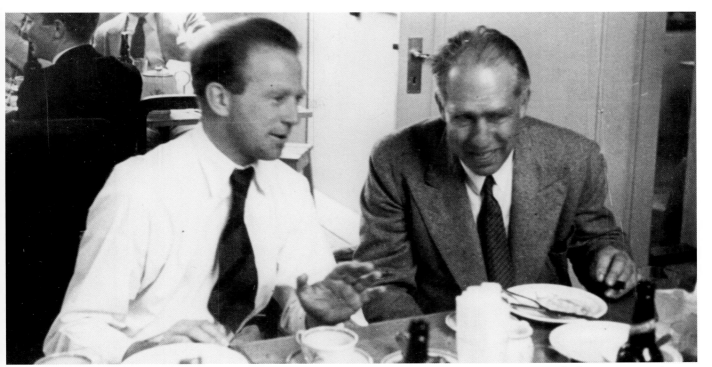

Werner Heisenberg, 1901–1976, left, one of the creators of quantum theory, with his mentor Niels Bohr, 1885–1962, the first person to apply quantum ideas to atoms. Heisenberg was the first to incorporate neutrons into a model of nuclei. (AIP Emilio Segrè Visual Archives.)

Further quantum weirdness

In diffraction experiments, the regular array of atoms in the crystal determines the final pattern. Somehow each photon has to 'see' the crystal as a whole – even if it turns up at a single point on the screen. Try to determine exactly where the photon went through the crystal, however, and the diffraction pattern is destroyed. It is as if the photon fills a large volume; yet when it is detected, it is found at particular point. This is one consequence of Heisenberg's Uncertainty Principle – a law that affects absolutely everything in the sub-microscopic world (see **Werner Heisenberg**).

Quantum effects are not just confined to photons – electrons, protons and neutrons behave in the same strange way too, which is one reason why it is so hard to visualize what an atom really looks like.

Electrons orbit the nucleus, but not in a manner that resembles a miniature Solar System of planets orbiting a sun, as suggested by the cartoons (see **Bohr's models** in chapter 2). If electrons behaved like planets, they would pass through a sequence of precise and measurable positions. The position of an electron can only be given as a probability; an electron does not *have* a precise position until we try to measure where it is. Moreover, just as trying to measure where the X-ray passed through the crystal destroys the diffraction pattern, so measuring the position of an electron will almost certainly knock it right out of the atom.

There is scarcely a more natural idea than that an object can be located at a certain place; an idea that has risen from our experience of everyday objects. The new quantum view of the world forces us to rethink what is meant by 'position'. In the case of the electron, all we can do is predict the likelihood of

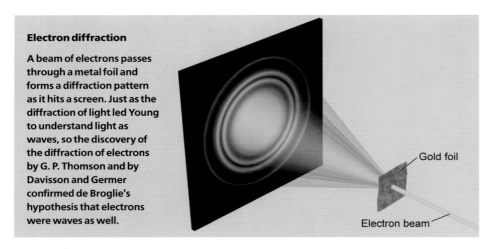

Electron diffraction

A beam of electrons passes through a metal foil and forms a diffraction pattern as it hits a screen. Just as the diffraction of light led Young to understand light as waves, so the discovery of the diffraction of electrons by G. P. Thomson and by Davisson and Germer confirmed de Broglie's hypothesis that electrons were waves as well.

Gold foil

Electron beam

the electron being found at a given place in an atom. This is not due to any shortcomings in our theories or measuring instruments, but rather because it is a property of Nature itself at this minuscule scale.

The wave-like behaviour of electrons, electron diffraction, can also be exploited to measure the size of nuclei and the structure of crystals. In a similar manner to X-rays, predictable and repeatable diffraction patterns can be built up spot by spot on a photographic film when beams of high energy electrons interact with the nuclei in a target, although there is just no way of predicting where a particular electron will leave its mark.

Electrons and photons do not have a monopoly on quantum weirdness. All atomic and nuclear particles, including protons and neutrons, exhibit the same schizophrenic behaviour we call wave–particle duality. Sometimes they behave like a wave and show diffraction effects, and at other times they behave like particles, see **Electron diffraction**.

Since 1925, physicists have come to accept that the world of atoms and nuclei is utterly different from the familiar world of objects measured in metres and centimetres. One of the pioneers of quantum theory, Niels Bohr, once said: "If you're not shocked by quantum mechanics, you don't understand it." Another legendary physicist, Richard Feynman, went further, claiming that no one understands quantum mechanics. Certainly, physicists who use quantum physics every day still find it deeply puzzling.

Living the half life

Radioactivity provides a clear example of the concept of indeterminacy; that is, identical initial situations lead to different outcomes. Consider a million identical uranium nuclei, identical in a way that goes beyond the everyday meaning. They are not just identical in the sense that toothbrushes coming off a production line are the same, the nuclei are indistinguishable by any conceivable measurement. These nuclei are also unstable, and undergo radioactive decay, but they do not decay in an identical time. All that can be said is that they have an equal likelihood of decaying in a given interval of time.

After a certain time (the half-life), half of the nuclei will have decayed, but there is no way of predicting when a particular uranium nucleus will decay (see **Nuclear half-life**). However, one interesting aspect of determinism does hold true: if we take another large sample of uranium nuclei then it will take

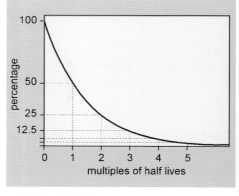

Nuclear half-life

After a time equal to one 'half life', half of the nuclei will have decayed. After two half-lives, only a quarter remain. After three, only an eighth is left, and so on.

the same length of time for half of it to decay as it took for the first sample. We can imagine a way to avoid the indeterminism in the decay of a nucleus if the unpredictable nature of decay is only a matter of our ignorance. Perhaps all the seemingly identical uranium nuclei are not identical after all. Rather, they have some kinds of unobservable characteristics that distinguish them from each other. These 'hidden variables' would be locked away inside each individual uranium nucleus, telling it when to decay.

However, most physicists are these days convinced that Nature does not resort to hidden variables to explain the unpredictable behaviour of radioactive decay. We just have to live with the idea that Nature is unpredictable.

Nuclear transformations

'Taking a quantum leap' is an expression that has filtered into everyday language – but what does it mean? Quantum leaps are another way the quantum world differs from our familiar world of human-sized objects. Although the energy associated with an atomic or nuclear quantum leap is minute by human standards, it is typically large on the atomic or nuclear scale. Certainly, it is very different from a process in which energy appears to change continuously, as we shall see.

Once again the radioactive decay of nuclei provides a window into the quantum world of the very small, including quantum leaps. Look at the photograph **Making tracks.** Remarkably, a single particle emitted by a nucleus can leave a visible trail in a cloud chamber. The photograph shows trails left by alpha particles emerging from nuclei as they undergo a transformation in which enough energy is given to the alpha particles to leave the trails that you see. A great deal of information can be determined from the tracks, including the energy of the particle. The particles with the highest energy leave the longest trails: they travel the furthest before slowing down and coming to a halt. Close measurement of tracks in cloud chambers reveal some alpha particles possess a little bit less energy than others.

Making tracks

Each of these tracks is a trail of tiny water droplets left by a single alpha particle passing through a cloud chamber. These tracks are evidence of particles, but to understand how alpha particles are emitted from nuclei, they must be treated as waves.

Double-sided silicon strip detector

Below is a double sided silicon strip detector, DSSSD. The DSSSD can register both the position and energy of a charged particle incident upon it. One side registers the position in one direction and the other side registers the position in the perpendicular direction.

Using silicon detectors

When an energetic particle from an accelerator strikes a nucleus in a target, several charged particles often emerge. An array of DSSSDs allows the energies and directions of the charged particles produced in such a reaction to be measured, yielding invaluable information about nuclear processes. In this picture, a beam of particles enters from top left and strikes a target that would be placed at the centre of the square array of 4 DSSSDs. They would all be in a high vacuum when operating.

Measuring the energy of the alpha particles is very important, and cloud chambers have long since been replaced by silicon detectors. A modern silicon detector is shown in **Double-sided silicon strip detector**, and in **Using silicon detectors** an array of four is shown arranged about a point in a vacuum scattering chamber where an incoming beam would strike a target. These are rather special silicon chips that give an electrical signal when a nuclear particle hits them. This signal allows the energy of the particle to be measured very accurately. Results from silicon detectors confirm that some alpha particles have a little less energy than others. The energies differ by distinct amounts so that some get progressively less than the maximum energy. An important physical concept that is employed here is the law of conservation of energy. Richard Feynman called it the cornerstone of physics. It means that the total energy of a system is always the same. If some alpha particles, emitted by exactly the same kind of nuclei, have a little less energy than the others, then the missing energy must stay in the so-called daughter nucleus: the nucleus left behind when the alpha particle is emitted, see **Ground state and excited state**.

The energy the alpha particle has as it flies out of a nucleus comes from nuclear energy that is normally locked away inside the nucleus. Since the alpha particles only ever come out with one of a set of distinct energies, then the daughter nucleus left behind can only have one of a set of certain values of energy. These values are known as energy levels and are often represented symbolically in diagrams by a series of horizontal lines. The fact that a nucleus can exist only in a series of distinct energies is an example of a new universal property. What is true of the daughter nucleus created in alpha decay is true of all nuclei, as well as of atoms and molecules. All these tiny objects can possess any one of a series of fixed amounts of energy, known as energy states. It is only when we compare this with everyday life that we realize just how strange it is.

Think of a car. The faster it moves, the more energy it has. In principle it can have any energy up to the energy corresponding to its top speed. Now imagine that the fuel runs out when the car reaches top speed. It slows down, passing continuously through all possible energies until it comes to a halt. It does not slow down in discrete steps and there are no missing energies that are avoided as the speed decreases.

Alternatively, imagine a red-hot poker cooling down. Since heat is a form of energy, the poker loses energy as it cools, but it does not cool down by stopping at a particular temperature and then jumping to a lower one. It cools continuously, passing through all possible temperatures on the way. This is so familiar that we never feel the need to call it a 'no-jump' process.

In the atomic world, nuclei do jump in energy. If a nucleus emits an alpha particle with less than the maximum possible energy, the daughter nucleus is left with a certain amount of extra energy above its 'ground state' (when it has the lowest energy possible). The daughter is said to be in an 'excited state'. So, unlike the car or the red-hot poker, it loses energy by jumping to a state with lower energy. It might do this several times until it eventually reaches the ground state.

With each jump, it gets rid of a packet of its energy. This energy packet is none other than a gamma ray photon. Most of the clicks a uranium prospector

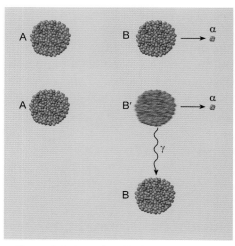

Ground state and excited state

Often, when nucleus A emits an alpha particle (α), the resulting nucleus B has no surplus energy. We say that it is in its 'ground state' and the alpha particle has the maximum energy. However, sometimes, as in the lower picture, the new nucleus is in an excited state. In this case the surplus energy is later thrown off in the form of a gamma ray (γ).

hears coming from a Geiger counter are caused by gamma ray emission, a secondary effect of the alpha decay process. Most alpha particles themselves do not penetrate through the walls of the Geiger counter. The term 'quantum leap' refers to the way the nucleus loses energy by discrete amounts rather than smoothly, but the energy lost by a single nucleus is absolutely minute compared to the energy required to make a cup of coffee. A quantum leap does not actually mean a big jump by the standards of the visible world around us – the colloquial meaning of the phrase. However, 'quantum leap' captures the idea that the nucleus undergoes a discontinuous change in energy – and also a discontinuous change in its structure. The atomic kind of quantum leap occurs on a very short timescale: sometimes a million millionth (10^{-12}) of a second after the one before, and sometimes a thousand times less (10^{-15} of a second).

Excited nuclei

Almost all nuclei have a series of excited states, such as that shown in **Ground state and excited state**. The only exceptions are the few that are so fragile that they break up if they have too much energy. An example of such a fragile nucleus is the nucleus of deuterium, or heavy hydrogen, consisting of just a proton and a neutron bound together very weakly.

Each nucleus, with a particular number of protons and neutrons, has its own unique pattern of possible excited energies. These 'fingerprints' are important in applications ranging from medicine to archaeology. Alpha decay is not the only process that can leave a nucleus in an excited state. Energy can be given directly to nuclei, for example, by bombarding them with fast particles from accelerators. The key point is that if a nucleus does find itself in a highly excited state then it will decay via a cascade of energy jumps, called transitions, until it reaches its lowest energy state.

When a nucleus makes a quantum leap between states, a gamma ray is emitted which carries off the energy difference between the states. These gamma ray energies can be measured very accurately with special detectors, see box **Measuring gamma rays**. The particular pattern of gamma ray energies emit-

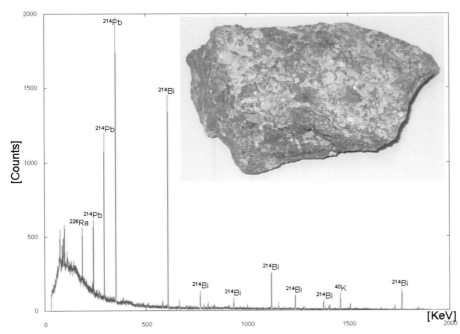

Measuring gamma rays

A piece of uranium ore and the spectrum of gamma rays coming from it as measured with a germanium detector. The gamma rays do not come from the uranium, but from the chain of short-lived daughter nuclei following the alpha decay of the uranium. The picture shows gamma rays from ^{226}Ra, ^{214}Pb, ^{214}Bi. The highest energy gamma ray that is shown is from the bismuth isotope, ^{214}Bi, and the lowest energy gamma ray that is labelled is from ^{226}Ra. The different gamma ray lines, corresponding to different energies, can be compared to the different coloured lines of a visible spectrum. The energy of gamma rays is defined in the box eV, keV, MeV, GeV.

ted by a nucleus, the gamma ray spectrum of the nucleus, allows a positive identification of the nucleus. Explaining the details of such a spectrum is a challenge to our theoretical understanding of nuclei, and the source of much that we know about nuclei.

The same idea also applies to atoms and molecules where the energy of the emitted light corresponds to frequencies spanning the visible part of the electromagnetic spectrum. Green fireworks, for example, are that colour because they contain copper which has prominent green frequencies in its atomic spectrum, and when a pan of boiling, salted water spills onto a gas flame, the flame appears yellow due to the sodium in the salt. This property is extraordinarily useful to astronomers who can use the spectra of atoms to determine what elements exist in distant stars and galaxies. They can also determine how common different elements are in the Universe.

Closer to home, some archaeologists study data from the spectra of the gamma rays emitted from nuclei. These nuclear archaeologists can determine the precise location where an artefact was made.

Wave–particle duality

Alpha particle radioactivity is a window into the strange behaviour of sub-atomic matter. What we have glimpsed through that window is so strange that there is still great debate about what it all really means today, a century after quantum physics was born. A natural reaction to hearing about the mysterious behaviour of the quantum world is to ask if it can really be like that. Yes, it can – there is now indisputable evidence that particles can sometimes behave like waves, and vice versa.

In alpha decay, both alpha particles and photons exhibit dual wave–particle behaviour. When a nucleus emits an alpha particle, the new nucleus which is formed may well be in an excited state in which case it will lose the excess energy by emitting packets of electromagnetic energy: gamma ray photons. Being electromagnetic radiation, gamma rays exhibit all the usual properties of waves; in particular they can create diffraction patterns. They also sometimes behave like particles: each photon is a package of energy and gives a single click in a Geiger counter, a pulse in a germanium crystal, or blackens a single grain on a photographic plate.

We have seen that alpha particles are helium ions, the very dense, electrically charged nuclei left after helium atoms have been stripped of their electrons. So far, we have concentrated on the *particle* nature of alpha particles. Each tiny flash of light on a zinc sulphide screen, that eventually led Rutherford to his model of the nucleus, marked the impact of an individual alpha particle. Similarly the tracks left in a cloud chamber are the result of particle behaviour. Yet alpha particles are as much waves as photons. Over the years there have been many experiments in which high energy alpha particles have been seen to give rise to diffraction patterns when they collide with other nuclei.

If you find the fact that waves can leave tracks in a cloud chamber deeply puzzling, you are not alone. Einstein wrestled on and off through the first two decades of the twentieth century with a similar problem related to light. He was very well aware of how electromagnetic waves are emitted from a source.

eV, keV, MeV and GeV

A convenient unit of energy used in atomic and nuclear physics is the electron volt, eV. That is the energy an electron gains when accelerated by a voltage of one volt. It is a small unit, so keV (kilo electron volt), see **Speaking of size** on page 16), MeV (mega electron volt) and GeV (giga electron volt) are also used. The energies of atomic states are usually measured in eV, but nuclear energies are typically a million times higher, so MeV is a common energy unit for nuclear energies. For the high energy particles produced by large accelerators like the LHC at CERN, GeV or TeV (tera electron volt or a trillion electron volts) are appropriate.

Henry Gwyn Jeffreys Moseley, 1887–1915. (AIP Emilio Segrè Visual Archives, W.F. Meggers collection.)

Think for a moment about a radio signal: radio waves are emitted in all directions from an antenna. This must be the same for atoms radiating visible light and for nuclei emitting gamma rays, and yet when photons are detected, they seem to have travelled in some specific direction to arrive at a point.

Many great names of physics have struggled with this problem. Today the process is explained by the wave 'collapsing', and we can do no better than quote the perplexed letter of the great physicist **Henry Gwyn Jeffreys Moseley**, who was killed very young at Gallipoli in 1915, ten years before the advent of quantum theory in its modern form:

"The X-ray problem is becoming intensely interesting. We have now got what seems to be definite proof that an X-ray, which spreads out in spherical form from a source as a wave can, when it meets an atom, collect up all its energy from all round and concentrate it on the atom. It is as if when a circular wave on water met an obstacle the wave were all suddenly to travel around the circle and disappear and concentrate its energy on attacking the obstacle. Mechanically, of course, this is absurd, but mechanics have in this direction been for some time a broken reed."

Moseley was right. As far as atoms and nuclei are concerned, the mechanics of Newton is useless. In 1929 **Neville Francis Mott** showed how an alpha particle "emitted as a spherical wave from a nucleus" can do much as Moseley surmised, and form a track in a cloud chamber. Although we now have a mathematical picture that can predict what happens when an alpha particle is emitted from a nucleus, a full understanding of what those equations really mean is still elusive. Most physicists would agree that this interplay of particle and wave properties is still as deeply mysterious as ever.

The work that originally convinced physicists that alpha particles can behave as waves was a crucial calculation carried out by **George Gamow**, and also by Gurney and Condon in 1928, which brilliantly solved a long standing puzzle concerning the properties of alpha decay. The puzzle was to explain a long-known fact about alpha decay: the half-life for alpha decay of a particular nucleus depends upon the energy released by that decay in a very particular way. This applies to all the dozens of known cases of alpha decay and is such that a small increase in energy released can make the half-life billions of times shorter. Gamow used quantum theory, involving the wave properties of alpha particles, to explain this. This theory involved a remarkable process called quantum tunnelling, to which we return in Chapter 5. Quantum tunnelling has other wide-ranging implications and plays a key part in explaining where the Sun gets its energy (see Chapter 9).

Before the work of Gamow, and of Gurney and Condon, it was not known whether the new quantum theory that worked so well for atoms would also work for nuclei. After all, nuclei are typically tens of thousands times smaller than atoms. Now there is no doubt.

Nevill Francis Mott, 1905–1996, driving, was one of the first to show how alpha particles, described by waves in alpha decay, appear as particle-like tracks in a cloud chamber. (AIP Emilio Segrè Visual Archives, courtesy Sir Nevill Mott.)

George Gamow, 1904–1968, whose work in 1928 showed that alpha particles can behave as waves. In so doing, he solved the long-standing puzzle about the half-life of alpha decay. This demonstrated for the first time that quantum mechanics applies to nuclei. (AIP Emilio Segrè Visual Archives.)

4. Measuring nuclei
Determining the shape and size of minute objects

One of the most basic properties of nuclei is their size, and measuring something thousands of times smaller than the atoms of the measuring instruments poses problems. Yet by 1911 Rutherford knew something about the size of atomic nuclei. His discovery that they were some 10,000 times smaller than the atoms that contained them was due to the remarkable way that alpha particles scatter from metal foils. Nature had given us a wonderful and unexpected gift – a completely new way to learn about the deep secrets of matter.

Today we can go a long way towards determining the exact sizes and shapes of nuclei. What has been learned about nuclear sizes has become a cornerstone of our understanding of atoms. How this knowledge has been achieved is a story in which the oddness of the quantum realm plays an important part.

Mega-microscopes

Previously we have described how it is not feasible to use ordinary microscopes in order to see objects smaller than a certain size. Instead, we depend on electron microscopes – which rely on the wave nature of electrons – to resolve objects as tiny as a virus, and even individual atoms. In effect, an electron microscope uses 'matter waves' instead of light waves (see **Diffraction**).

As de Broglie first showed, the wavelength associated with moving particles becomes shorter as the energy of the particles is increased, and this is certainly true for electrons. For use in a microscope, electrons need to be given enough energy to make their wavelength shorter than the details of the object under study. It is a big step from viewing viruses or individual atoms to seeing atomic nuclei, but it is one that has been taken. For achieving this step, a pioneer of the art, **Robert Hofstadter**, was awarded the Nobel prize in physics in 1961.

Hofstadter thought big. He had to, because the laws of physics demanded that large machines – what we might call 'mega-microscopes' – are needed to produce electrons with high enough energies to penetrate the secrets of the nucleus. The accelerators developed at Stanford University in California, and elsewhere were on a vastly greater scale than the source of electrons in a electron microscope.

To understand how it is possible to gain an idea of the size of nuclei by observing matter waves, consider what happens when sea waves wash up against a hole in a breakwater. The smaller the hole, the more the waves are scattered, or spread out, on the other side. If you did not know the size of the hole, you could, in principle, work it out from seeing how the waves behave. If the distance between successive wave crests (the wavelength) is too large, then you do not get a pattern at all.

Robert Hofstadter, 1915–1990, pioneered the use of electrons for studying the size and density of nuclei and of the nucleons they are made of. (Copyright the Nobel Foundation.)

Diffraction

Waves 'diffract' (spread out) when they strike objects or pass through holes or slits in barriers. On the right is shown how the smaller the object or the hole relative to the wavelength, the stronger the diffraction, provided the object or hole is not much smaller than the wavelength. To study nuclei, we need much shorter wavelengths than can be achieved with an electron microscope.

In a similar manner, light waves can produce a diffraction pattern when shone through various tiny holes. Again we can work out the size of the hole from the different patterns of light and dark rings.

We saw in Chapter 3 how electrons behave as waves when passing through a metal foil. They give a diffraction pattern from which the arrangement of atoms in the foil can be deduced. In the 1950s, Hofstadter and his colleagues built an accelerator that gave electrons millions of times the energy available to G. P. Thomson, and thousands of times higher than those in the electron microscope. The much slower electrons that gave the diffraction patterns (see page 38) revealed the spacing of the atoms in the foil, but these high energy electrons were too fast to be scattered by the spread out atoms –they were diffracted by the much smaller nuclei. From the resulting diffraction patterns, the size of atomic nuclei could be deduced. It was a great act of faith when Hofstadter and his colleagues asked for the large sums of money needed to build the large electron accelerators, but their faith was to be rewarded.

Another quantum concept

Many common words do not mean quite the same when applied to atoms and nuclei as they do for everyday objects and 'size' is one of these words. This is because, in the quantum world, objects such as nuclei simply cannot ever have sharp edges. Size is generally defined as the distance from one edge of an object to the other. If it does not have a definite edge, then defining its size is not clear-cut.

Nuclei are composed of protons and neutrons (nucleons) which obey the laws of quantum mechanics. According to these laws, we simply cannot say where a nucleon is in a nucleus; we can only say how likely it is to be found at a given point. As a result, atomic nuclei are fuzzy.

The laws of quantum mechanics are far from only about uncertainty: in fact, they tell us just how likely it is to find a nucleon in a given place. If you select some point in a nucleus, quantum mechanics determines the probability of a nucleon being at that point. This probability does not suddenly become zero at some particular distance from the nuclear centre. If it did, then that distance would be a sharp surface of the nucleus. Instead, nuclei have a diffuse (fuzzy) surface in which the probability of finding a nucleon drops off gradually. The box **Nuclear density** illustrates this for a typical nucleus, though slightly exaggerated for clarity. The graph at the top shows how the density of nucleons is a maximum at the nuclear centre (zero radius) and decreases until it becomes zero further out. The bottom part of the figure suggests how the density of protons (red) and neutrons (blue) thins out gradually, leading to the diffuse surface.

Measuring fuzzy nuclei

How can this diffuse nuclear surface be measured? A proton carries positive electric charge, so the more likely that protons will be at a particular point in the nucleus, the more charge there will be at that point. The positive electric charge on the nucleus must therefore also be spread out in a way that has a fuzzy edge. Since electrons are electrically charged, a high speed electron moving through a nucleus is deflected by the positive charge in a way that depends on how that charge is distributed. This allows us to use a beam of electrons to measure a nucleus. It does not matter that the electron is unaware of the neutrons in the nucleus; it is sufficient that protons and neutrons are distributed in the same way, a good assumption for many nuclei.

Since electrons behave like waves, a beam of them striking a nucleus will produce a diffraction pattern. Although the electrons are detected as particles, the pattern is produced because greater numbers will be detected at certain angles and fewer at other angles. For water waves, both a barrier and a hole produce quite sharp diffraction patterns, but the patterns left by electrons scattering from nuclei are less distinct. The difference is that the hole and the barrier in the water have sharp edges and the water waves either pass through completely or not at all, but the fuzzy edge of the nucleus causes a gradual change in the quantity of deflected electrons. The details of the electron diffraction pattern reveal how the nuclear charge is spread out and we can determine just how fuzzy the nucleus is. The box **Measuring nuclei with electrons** shows the idea of how the diffraction pattern is measured by counting the number of electrons detected at a particular angle, and the box **Electron diffraction patterns** shows some examples.

The size of atomic nuclei

To compare nuclear sizes we have to define what is meant by the word 'size' when applied to these diffuse objects. From electron scattering, we find that heavier nuclei, in spite of having fuzzy surfaces, have a rather constant density over the central region. This central density is much the same for a wide range of nuclei. This allows a nuclear radius to be defined in spite of the fuzzy edge. The nuclear radius is the distance from the centre of the nucleus to a point where the density is half that at the centre. Some examples of nuclear densities measured by electron scattering are shown in **Measured by eletrons**.

Apart from the diffuse surface, all nuclei have about the same density. This can be deduced from the way that the volume of the nucleus depends on the number of nucleons it contains. Thus if nucleus A has twice the radius of nucleus B, then nucleus A will have eight times (2 x 2 x 2) as many protons and neutrons as nucleus B. This is what is expected of everyday material that cannot be compressed. If a solid ball has twice the radius of another made of

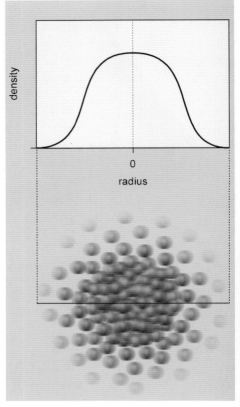

Nuclear density

At the centre of a nucleus the protons and neutrons are quite densely packed. The density falls off further out, but there is no sharp nuclear edge. The line on the graph indicates the nuclear density: how many nucleons there would be in a small volume at a given distance from the nuclear centre.

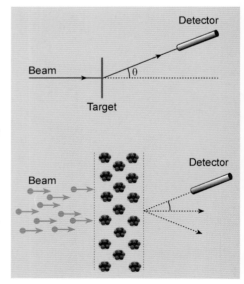

Measuring nuclei with electrons

Hofstadter and his colleagues measured nuclei in a thin foil by firing a beam of electrons at it, counting the electrons scattered in each direction with an array of detectors.

the same material, it would have eight times the mass. The volume, and hence mass, of a spherical object is proportional to the cube of its radius. This is illustrated in the box **Number of nucleons and nuclear size**. Because nuclei obey this rule, we can deduce that all nuclei are made out of incompressible material of the same density. Atoms, however, are quite different.

It is remarkable that atoms and their nuclei behave in opposite ways: to a first approximation, atoms of different mass all have the same size and therefore different densities, whereas nuclei of different mass have the same density and therefore different sizes. There are exceptions in both cases: for instance alkali atoms like sodium are larger, and halogens like chlorine are smaller, but the difference is not dramatic. The fact that all atoms do not have the same density is crucial; if atoms of magnesium and of lead had identical density, then equal amounts of magnesium and lead material would also have the same density. We know this is not true – magnesium sinkers are not used for fishing, and lead wheels are inappropriate for fast cars!

For nuclei, however, the converse is true. A plutonium nucleus, which has about 240 protons and neutrons, has about twice the radius of a nickel nucleus containing an eighth as many protons and neutrons. This is because both nuclei have similar density, a density they share with almost all nuclei. The exception to this rule of uniform density is found in some remarkable cases that have caused a stir in recent years – the so-called 'halo nuclei', discussed

Electron diffraction patterns

Just as the amplitudes of the waves at different angles allow the size of the hole to be measured (see **Diffraction**, page 45), so the number of electrons found at each angle allow the size of the nucleus to be deduced. The energy of the incident electrons is in mega electron volts (MeV). For example. 360 MeV is the energy of an electron that has been accelerated by an electric voltage of 360 million volts.

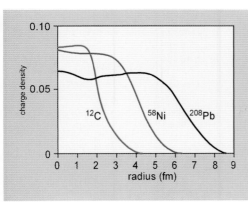

Measured by electrons

The lines show how the density of charge varies from the centre of the nucleus outwards. The nickel (Ni) nucleus of 58 nucleons is clearly larger than the carbon (C) nucleus of 12 nucleons, and the lead (Pb) nucleus of 208 nucleons is the largest.

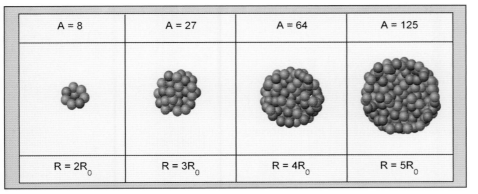

Numbers of nucleons and nuclear size

How does the nuclear radius depends on the number of nucleons? Most nuclei have much the same density, so their volume is proportional to the number of nucleons. As a result, the cube of the radius is also proportional to the number of nucleons, as we see here.

later in this chapter. The density of a nucleus is enormous compared with everyday objects. If a solid football were made of pure nuclear matter, it would weigh as much as Mt Everest.

Measuring nuclei with lasers

To measure nuclei using electrons, a target containing the atoms whose nuclei are to be measured has to be made, but not all nuclei are sufficiently stable to sit in a target long enough for such experiments to be performed. There is a need to study such short-lived nuclei; they may well have different properties from stable nuclei, in which case a completely biased view of nuclear sizes would be obtained if only stable nuclei were studied. Other ways are therefore needed to measure nuclei.

There is a method that allows the measurement of nuclei that exist only fleetingly. It is based on the fact that, although the electrons in an atom are spread out through a vastly greater volume of space than the nucleus itself, there is nevertheless some probability that they can exist at the centre of the atom in the space occupied by the nucleus. This modifies the wavelengths of the light given out by the atom in a way that depends on the size of the nucleus. The effect is tiny, but lasers allow us to measure the wavelengths with incredible precision – enough precision, in fact, to turn the tiny effects of different nuclear sizes into a practical way of measuring them.

This method of measuring nuclei, carried out at **ISOLDE** for example, is known as the 'isotope shift method' because it is based on the way the wavelengths of light emitted by an atom varies from one isotope of the element to the next. Since different isotopes of the same element have the same number of electrons (and protons), their electrons will be distributed in almost exactly the same way. Where they do differ is in the number of neutrons their nuclei contain, and this affects the size of the nuclei. Thus the light emitted by their electrons will differ very slightly due to the manner in which the electrons' probability distributions overlap the different-sized nuclei.

The difference in the wavelengths of light for different isotopes can be used to determine the variation in size of the nuclei. As long as the size of the nucleus of a stable isotope can be determined, for example by using the Hofstadter method of electron scattering, then the sizes of all the other isotopes of that element can be deduced.

Nuclear shapes

It is a natural assumption to imagine nuclei as tiny spheres. In the 1930s, even before lasers were invented, crude isotope shift measurements were used on different isotopes of the fairly rare element, samarium (Sm). They showed that nuclei of the heavier samarium isotopes appeared larger than expected. We now know this is because there is a jump between spherical and non-spherical between ^{150}Sm and ^{152}Sm; the two extra neutrons change the shape of the nucleus, making it seem larger to the atomic electrons. Today it is known that quite a large proportion of nuclei have non-spherical shapes. Such nuclei are said to be *deformed*.

Most of our evidence about nuclear shapes arises from the fact that non-spherical nuclei can be made to spin. Another rather odd quantum concept is

Ben Mottelson, 1926–, American-born physicist living in Denmark. He was awarded the Nobel Prize in 1975 with James Rainwater, 1917–1986, and Aage Bohr, 1922 –2009, the son of Niels Bohr, for work on vibrations and rotations of nuclei. (Copyright the Nobel Foundation.)

that if a quantum object, such as a nucleus, is perfectly spherical, then there is nothing to distinguish its orientation in space. As a result, spherical nuclei cannot be said to rotate.

But some nuclei certainly can be made to rotate, and the more deformed a nucleus is, the more easily it can be made to rotate. This rotation is another way in which the nucleus can gain energy – energy that it can lose by emitting gamma rays and hence slowing down. The more deformed it is, the more quickly a spinning nucleus slows down by radiating gamma rays. This leads to a method for measuring how much nuclei deviate from the spherical. The procedure is to measure how easily nuclei are set spinning when other nuclei are fired at them, or by determining just how quickly spinning nuclei slow down by emitting gamma rays. A major contributor to our understanding of nuclear deformation was **Ben Mottelson.**

Most nuclei have one of two basic shapes (see **Nuclear deformation**). They are either spherical or prolate (shaped like an American football). An important exception is the nuclei of carbon, which are oblate (like a squashed sphere; the Earth is slightly oblate – squashed at the poles). Both prolate and oblate nuclei are nearly always symmetric about their long axis (if prolate) or short axis (if oblate).

Quantum mechanics has another trick up its sleeve concerning deformed nuclei. A deformed nucleus can no more lie with its long axis fixed pointing in a given direction than a proton or neutron can sit still at some fixed point within the nucleus. Both are a result of the Heisenberg Uncertainty Principle. Thus, the long axis of a prolate nucleus has equal probability of pointing in every direction. In other words it is pointing in all directions at once!

If an isotope shift experiment is performed on an atom containing a prolate nucleus, the electrons in the atom see an even fuzzier nucleus than usual. The tip of the long axis of the nucleus traces out a larger volume of space than any point on the surface of a spherical nucleus with the same mass because it lies farther out. As a result, the surface is even more spread out than for a spherical nucleus, causing a shift in the spectra. The box **Mercury isotopes** presents an interesting case: we see that **ISOLDE** measurements reveal a rapid alteration in size among the lighter isotopes of mercury.

Modern experiments reveal more about the shape of deformed nuclei than just whether they are prolate or oblate. Amongst the many nuclei which are strongly deformed are the isotopes of uranium and plutonium, a fact important for the process of nuclear fission. Some nuclei can exist in states of different shapes, see **A nucleus with three shapes**.

Super-deformed nuclei

Most prolate-shaped nuclei are only slightly deformed. However, in the mid 1980s, physicists at the Daresbury Laboratory in the UK discovered a remarkable phenomenon: super-deformation. Sometimes nuclei are twice as long as they are wide.

When nuclei rotate they have a tendency to stretch. This is due to the same force you feel when sitting in a fast car as it turns a tight corner. Nuclei are generally too tough to stretch very much, but at Daresbury it was found that if certain nuclei are made to rotate really fast, it is as if something suddenly gives and the stretching force takes them into an entirely new shape. Such nuclei have become super-deformed. As they slow down, by emitting lots of gamma rays, the nuclei revert back to the normal deformed or even spherical shapes.

The discovery of super-deformation was made possible by the development of very elaborate arrays of gamma ray detectors. First, nuclei need to be super-deformed by exciting them to high energy. This is done by bombarding them in a target with other nuclei accelerated to high energies in a particle accelerator. Each excited nucleus then emits a cascade of gamma rays as it jumps down in energy to its state of lowest energy. From the energy of these gamma rays, the deformation can be deduced, but the catch is that all the gamma rays from a nucleus need to be measured. To do this, the nuclei have to be surrounded by gamma ray detectors, all connected to sophisticated electronics and computers. One half of one such an array of gamma detectors is shown in the box **Superdeformation: collecting the evidence of the gamma rays**. A schematic picture, **Gamma detector arrangement**

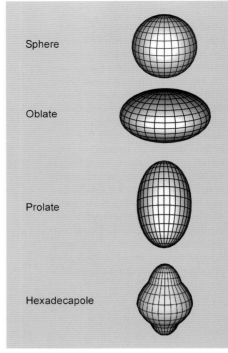

Nuclear deformation

Not all nuclei are spheres. A few are 'oblate', that is, flattened at the poles, and a great many are 'prolate', lengthened in the direction of the poles, like an American football. Quite subtle shapes can be measured, like the bottom figure which shows a 'hexadecapole' variant of prolate. These shapes are exaggerated for clarity.

Mercury isotopes

Mercury (Hg) isotopes with decreasing masses steadily decrease in radius. But at mass 186, 184 and 182, the removal of another neutron produces a jump in size. The anomalously large size of these nuclei is evidence that they are not spherical. These measurements were a triumph for ISOLDE. The isotope ^{185}Hg has an excited state which, unlike the ground state, has the normal size.

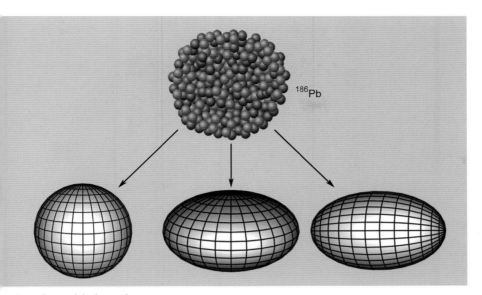

^{186}Pb

A nucleus with three shapes

When the isotope of polonium, ^{190}Po, undergoes alpha decay, the lead isotope ^{186}Pb is formed. This nucleus can exist in three forms, all with much the same energy: spherical (left), oblate (centre) and prolate (right).

Superdeformation, collecting the evidence of gamma rays

This shows half of an array of germanium detectors that, with another similar array, would form a ball of detectors completely surrounding the nuclei whose properties are being studied. This array, called Gammasphere, is at the Argonne National Laboratory in the USA. The whole array is arranged so that a beam from an accelerator strikes a target located at the centre of the array where the nucleus to be studied is created and then vanishes after a very brief existence. This gamma array is, in fact, an evolutionary descendant of those which originally discovered superdeformation in the 1980s, but the principle is the same, and many new nuclear phenomena have been discovered with such detectors.

shows a few gamma detectors (part of a complete array) pointing inwards towards the gamma-emitting nuclei.

Halo nuclei break the rules

Although most nuclei have much the same density, there are exceptions. One exceptional nucleus, the deuteron, has been studied for a long time. The deuteron is the nucleus of heavy hydrogen, consisting of just one proton and one neutron that are very weakly bound together. As a result of this weak binding, the proton and neutron have a significant probability of lying very far apart. The probability distribution of the deuteron extends out in space to such an extent that it has the same size as that of a very much heavier nucleus. This is where we catch another glimpse of how strange the quantum world is: the proton and neutron spend part of the time outside the range of the force that holds them together, yet they still remain bound together unless the deuteron is hit by something like a powerful gamma ray.

Adding a second neutron to a deuteron makes a nucleus of tritium, an even heavier isotope of hydrogen. This extra neutron draws the original proton and neutron closer together so the tritium nucleus (a triton) is actually smaller than the deuteron. Adding a second proton to a triton continues this process, making a tightly bound helium nucleus – an alpha particle. The two protons and two neutrons in the alpha particle are so close together that this nucleus has much the same density as most heavier nuclei. In general, adding further protons or neutrons does not affect the nuclear density, but there are a few further exceptions.

In recent years a remarkable new class of nuclei has been discovered: the halo nuclei. The most famous is a lithium isotope with no less than eight neutrons accompanying its three protons. This is ^{11}Li. The last two neutrons in this nucleus are very weakly bound, and are spread out over a volume which extends far outside the range of the other nine nucleons. As a result, this nucleus extends as far out as a nucleus of lead with over 200 protons and neutrons, as you can see in the box **Halo Nuclei**. The graph at the bottom right hand of the box shows how the average radius of all the protons and neutrons in the lithium isotopes jumps up between ^{9}Li and ^{11}Li as the number of neutrons increases from 6 to 8. But, as the picture comparing ^{11}Li and the lead isotope with 208 nucleons suggests, this is not the whole story. The *average* radius of all the particles in ^{11}Li might be about 3.5 fm, but the last couple of neutrons extend out to 6 fm from the centre. It is in this sense that the ^{11}Li nucleus is about as large as a lead nucleus with 208 protons and neutrons. By the way, the last two neutrons don't lie in a ring with a radius of 6 fm. As we have seen, the strange laws of quantum mechanics do not allow us to pin down the position of a neutron, and the diagram is just meant to suggest that there is some probability of finding a neutron as far as 6 fm from the centre of the nucleus. This is a remarkable distance, and means that these neutrons have a good chance of being outside the range of the force that holds them in the nucleus!

The discovery of halo nuclei in the mid-1980s electrified the community of nuclear physicists. These nuclei present a rich variety of phenomena to study, and stretch our understanding of nuclei theory to the limits. They also inspired the development of new accelerators and also particle detectors,

Gamma detector arrangement

A schematic diagram showing how the germanium detectors are arranged in an array such as AGATA (the Advanced GAmma Tracking Array). The grey modules, pointing inwards, each contain a number of extremely pure germanium crystals. The green cylinders behind the detectors contain liquid nitrogen since the germanium must be kept very cold to suppress the background 'noise'. This diagram does not show the large number of cables required to carry the vast flow of data to the computers.

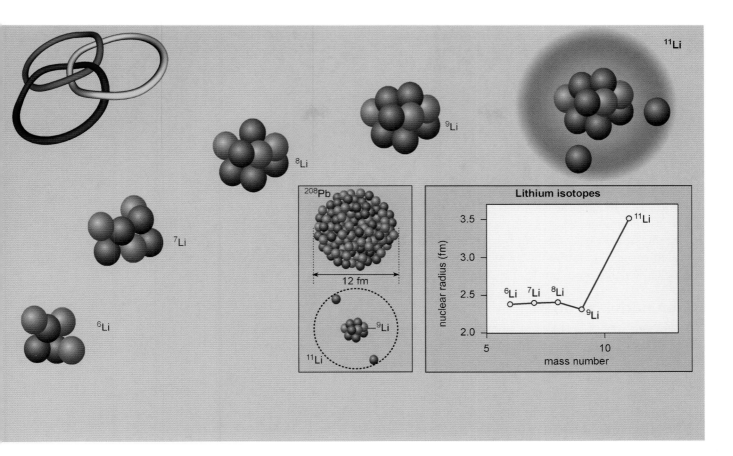

Halo nuclei

The isotope of lithium with three protons and six neutrons has just the size that would be expected for a nucleus with nine nucleons. There is no stable lithium nucleus with seven neutrons, but there is a lithium nucleus with eight neutrons ... and it stretches out as far as a lead nucleus. Its surface is very tenuous, containing just two neutrons in a large volume. Several of these 'halo nuclei' have now been found, and they present a huge challenge to experimenters and theorists struggling to understand their many strange properties. The Borromean rings at top left are such that if one is cut, all three fall apart. This is also true of the ^{9}Li core and two outer neutrons that make up the halo nucleus ^{11}Li. ^{10}Li does not exist, nor does a nucleus containing just two neutrons.

driven by the extremely fleeting existence of halo nuclei. Among the remarkable nuclei that have been discovered, are an isotope of helium with no less than 6 neutrons, ^{8}He (remember ordinary helium is ^{4}He) and an isotope of carbon with sixteen neutrons, ^{22}C. A ^{22}C nucleus has a lifetime of a few milliseconds (ordinary stable carbon is ^{12}C and the radioactive carbon used for dating is ^{14}C). These weird halo nuclei have inspired scientists who study atoms and molecules to look for halos there too.

5. Strange nuclear material
The contents of a nucleus

So far, an atomic nucleus has been described as a collection of Z protons and N neutrons. The protons each carry one unit of positive charge, whereas the neutrons are uncharged and are very slightly heavier than protons. A nucleus has been assumed to contain only protons and neutrons. However, we have revealed enough quantum mechanical surprises to suggest that, when it comes to nuclei, nothing is as simple as it seems.

When nuclei fall apart

The obvious way of finding out what nuclei are made of is to observe what particles they emit, either with or without external prompting. For example, a radioactive nucleus spontaneously ejects particles and changes into a different kind of nucleus. Stable nuclei, on the other hand, need inducement before they will eject particles. In fact, any nucleus can be broken apart by injecting energy, perhaps by hitting it hard enough with another nucleus. This can be done in the laboratory by using high energy particles from accelerators, but it also happens naturally in stars. When nuclei collide and produce new nuclei or other particles we have *nuclear reactions*, much studied in accelerator laboratories.

Nuclear reactions were important even before stars existed; all of the nuclear material appeared, in the form of the lightest nuclei, a few minutes after the Big Bang. At that time, the Universe was an extremely hot and crowded place, with nuclei being formed and, almost as fast, broken apart. Almost immediately, the Universe expanded and cooled sufficiently for nuclei not to be broken apart as soon as they were created. These surviving nuclei formed the primordial material (mostly hydrogen, helium and a bit of lithium) which eventually condensed into stars.

Radioactivity and the constitution of nuclei

The idea that most of the mass of atoms resides in compact nuclei was still years in the future when Rutherford first noticed that radioactivity involved two kinds of particles. It soon became clear that beta rays were J. J. Thomson's recently discovered electrons, since their paths were easily bent by magnetic fields in exactly the same way, see **Bending radiation**. Beta rays also penetrated matter much more readily than alpha particles. It took a little longer to identify alpha particles as helium nuclei, but this was finally established by Rutherford and Royds in 1908, see **The nature of alpha particles**.

One possible conclusion to be drawn from radioactivity is that atomic nuclei are made of alpha particles and electrons, but this would not work for hydrogen since the hydrogen nucleus has much less mass than an alpha particle. To solve this problem, a very old idea was revived: that all atoms are composed of multiples of hydrogen. This idea originated with William Prout in 1815, and is known as Prout's hypothesis. It was applied a hundred years later to nuclei

The nature of alpha particles

The apparatus used by Rutherford and Royds in 1908 to prove that alpha particles were helium ions (in modern terms: helium nuclei). Alpha particles penetrated through a thin window into a vacuum chamber. When an electric discharge was passed through this chamber the light given out was analysed by a spectroscope, which confirmed the presence of helium.

rather than atoms; all nuclei were predicted to be composed of various numbers of hydrogen nuclei (protons).

This theory cannot be quite right as, for example, the nucleus of a nitrogen atom has the mass of fourteen protons, but the charge of just seven protons. The textbooks of the 1920s had a simple answer to this: the nitrogen nucleus has fourteen protons and also seven electrons to balance out the charge of half the protons. After all, there must be electrons inside atomic nuclei since electrons come out of nuclei in beta decay.

In this proton–electron model, alpha particles would consist of four protons and two electrons. Many nuclei decay by ejecting this particular structure from the nucleus as a complete particle, so there must be something special about this configuration. Another feature also suggests the helium nucleus is somehow special: the most common isotopes of many light elements are apparently multiples of the alpha particle. By far the most common isotope of carbon, for example, is ^{12}C which has the same charge and mass as three alpha particles; ^{13}C is very uncommon and ^{14}C is unstable. The box **Alpha-like nuclei** shows how all the even-Z elements from carbon to calcium except argon, are predominantly alpha-like. From this, the alpha particle appears to be special in some way, and indeed some nuclei do contain alpha particles but not in a straightforward way, as we see at the end of this chapter.

Do nuclei contain electrons?

Like alpha particles, electrons appear to be ejected from nuclei. Unlike alpha particles, there is a very straightforward answer to the question of whether they exist in nuclei. They do not, and they cannot.

Firstly, the absence of electrons within nuclei can be understood from Heisenberg's Uncertainty Principle. This principle is commonly, and wrongly, taken to mean that everything on the microscopic level is uncertain. In fact, it implies that the more we try to localize a quantum particle such as an

^{12}C	^{16}O	^{20}Ne	^{24}Mg	^{28}Si	^{32}S	^{36}Ar	^{40}Ca
3α	4α	5α	6α	7α	8α	9α	10α
98.9%	99.8%	90.5%	79.0%	92.2%	95.0%	<1%	96.9%

Alpha-like nuclei

Do nuclei have alpha particles within them? By far the most common isotopes of all the even Z elements from carbon to sulphur have the same number of protons and neutrons as three, four, five etc. alpha particles. It is not true for argon for which ^{36}Ar has an abundance of less than 1 percent. These facts are best explained in terms of the energy valley (discussed in Chapter 6) and the tendency of protons and neutrons to pair up. Before the discovery of the neutron, it was natural to suppose that nuclei are composed of protons, electrons and alpha particles. The bottom line gives the percentage of the naturally occurring element that has the indicated alpha-like structure. For example, 92.2 percent of silicon atoms have a nucleus with the same number of protons and neutrons as seven alpha particles.

electron – that is to confine it to a smaller and smaller region of space – the larger the fluctuations in its motion due to the uncertainty in its momentum. The result is that for an electron to be confined to the tiny nucleus, its motion would be too violent for it to stay there for long. Protons on the other hand, which are nearly two thousand times heavier than electrons, can easily be confined to the volume of a nucleus since they move about more slowly and the uncertainty in their motion is much less.

Another argument against atomic nuclei having any electrons in them comes from the light emitted when an electric discharge is passed through nitrogen gas. The fine details in the pattern of spectral lines indicate clearly, according to certain quantum rules, that the nitrogen nucleus has an even number of particles, but if this nucleus is made of protons and electrons it would have to be an odd number: fourteen protons plus seven electrons.

In 1932, **James Chadwick**'s discovery of the neutron, which is a neutral particle with about the same mass as a proton, solved this problem. Werner Heisenberg then suggested, correctly, that atomic nuclei consist purely of protons and neutrons. Chadwick's discovery was to mark the beginning of modern nuclear physics. Now the nitrogen nucleus would have seven protons and seven neutrons: an even number of particles in total.

The following question demanded an answer: if nuclei consist of just protons and neutrons, where do the beta-decay electrons come from? Beta-decay electrons also posed another problem, one of the greatest problems of physics in the twentieth century, and a problem which drove physicists to desperate remedies.

Missing particles

Beta-decay electrons appeared to break the law of conservation of energy. The nucleus emitting the electron has a definite energy, and the nucleus produced in the decay has a definite energy, but the electrons emerge with a range of energies always less than the difference in energy between the initial and final nuclei. The missing amount of energy appeared to suggest

James Chadwick, 1891–1974. His discovery of the neutron in 1932 was a turning point in nuclear physics. Chadwick was well aware that the neutron had been predicted by Rutherford in 1920. In 1935, Chadwick received the Nobel prize in physics. (AIP Emilio Segrè Visual Archives.)

Wolfgang Pauli, 1900–1958, and Niels Bohr, 1885–1962. One of Pauli's many contributions to quantum physics concerned the spin of elementary particles such as electrons. The spin of much larger objects like this top was clearly also of great interest. (AIP Emilio Segrè Visual Archives.)

that energy is not always conserved in beta decay. However, the law of conservation of energy is a 'foundation stone of physics' and few physicists dared to speculate that there was an exception to the rule. Despite this, Niels Bohr did just that – and turned out to be wrong.

An alternative proposal, made by **Wolfgang Pauli** in 1930, was that a second, virtually undetectable particle was emitted at the same time as the electron. This new particle, later called a neutrino (meaning 'little neutral one'), shared energy with the electron in a random way such that the total energy of the two particles was equal to the difference in energy between the parent and daughter nuclei. In this manner, energy is conserved after all.

Pauli's idea was radical, but it became a key part of a theory of beta decay proposed by the brilliant Italian physicist, **Enrico Fermi**, in 1934. Over the years, Fermi's theory has been greatly extended and incorporated into more modern models, but still successfully accounts for a wide range of phenomena connected with beta decay. According to this theory, in a nucleus that has more than the ideal number of neutrons, a neutron turns into a proton, creating both an electron and a neutrino. Strictly speaking, electrons are accompanied by anti-neutrinos, the *anti*-particle of a neutrino. We discuss anti-particles below. In fact, the word 'neutrino' is often loosely used for anti-neutrinos as well as (true) neutrinos.

Enrico Fermi, 1901–1954, was unique in the 20th century for his eminence in both theoretical and experimental physics. (AIP Emilio Segrè Visual Archives.)

Neutrinos are exceptionally hard to detect. More than 150 million neutrinos pass through every square centimetre of your body every second, and even a body the size of the Earth will very rarely stop a neutrino. It is therefore not surprising that it was 1956 before Reines and Cowan could announce neutrinos had been positively detected. This was long after Pauli's speculation (1930) and Fermi's theory (1934), but proved that they had been correct. Today, neutrinos play a vital role in astronomy and cosmology as well as in nuclear physics.

Antimatter

Fermi's theory embodies one of the most revolutionary ideas of twentieth century physics: the number of fundamental particles in the world is not fixed. Electrons are not emitted from nuclei in beta decay, but are created, along with neutrinos. The idea that particles can be created was one consequence of combining quantum mechanics with Einstein's special theory of relativity, a feat achieved by **Paul Dirac**.

Combining relativity and quantum mechanics had another consequence: the existence of anti-particles. Dirac's theory predicted that for every kind of particle there is a corresponding anti-particle having the same mass. If the particle has an electric charge, the anti-particle has the opposite charge, but even neutral particles like neutrons have anti-particles. The anti-particle for the electron, called the positron, was discovered in 1932 by **Carl D. Anderson**, for which he received the Nobel prize in Physics in 1936 (see **Positron discovery**). It wasn't until 1955 that accelerators could supply enough energy to produce anti-protons. This was achieved by **Owen Chamberlain** and Emilio Segre at Berkeley in California, for which they received the Nobel prize in 1959. Nuclei with more than one nucleon also have anti-particles and anti-deuteron was discovered in 1965. However, the anti-alpha particle had to wait until 2011 to be created at RHIC near New York.

When a particle meets its anti-particle, they annihilate each other releasing pure energy that is carried off as radiation. The energy released is that predicted by Einstein's famous equation, $E=mc^2$. When an electron and a positron annihilate each other, for example, the energy released, E, is equal to their combined mass, m, multiplied by the square of the speed of light. The process of annihilation is reversible and, when a high energy photon, maybe from cosmic rays, interacts with a nucleus it quite often disappears, with its energy reappearing as two particles, an electron–positron pair.

Beta decay as it was originally discovered takes place when nuclei with too many neutrons correct the imbalance by transmuting a neutron into a proton, an electron and an anti-neutrino. Nuclei with the opposite imbalance, too many protons, decay in the opposite fashion: a proton is converted into a neutron, a positron and a neutrino. This kind of beta radioactivity was first discovered by Irène Joliot-Curie (Marie Curie's daughter) and Frederic Joliot in 1934 and is now of immense importance in modern medicine, particularly in positron emission tomography (known as PET for short). PET is a much used diagnostic tool, especially important for diagnosing brain disease.

We have met two forms of beta decay: (i) a neutron becomes a proton and an electron is emitted together with an anti-neutrino, and (ii) a proton becomes a neutron with the emission of a positron and a neutrino. There is actually another form of the second kind: *electron capture* in which one of the atomic electrons is captured by the nucleus so that a proton becomes a neutron and all the energy of the decay is carried off by a neutrino.

Chadwick's discovery of the neutron provided the foundations for a very successful picture of nuclear structure that has been the cornerstone of nuclear physics for many years. In this model, nuclei consist of protons and neutrons, and the emission of electrons and positrons does not mean that these particles are contained within them.

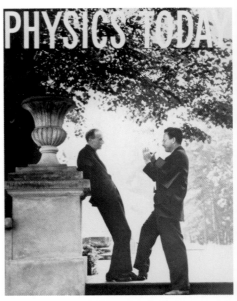

Paul Adrien Maurice Dirac, 1902–1984, left, and Richard P. Feynman, 1918–1988, on the cover of a magazine. Dirac was the first to successfully combine quantum theory and relativity; in doing so, he predicted the existence of positrons. Feynman developed a formalism for doing the very complex calculations involving electrons, positrons and light. (AIP Emilio Segrè Visual Archives.)

Positron discovery

The first evidence for the positron, the anti-particle of the electron. The cloud chamber track bends the wrong way in a magnetic field for it to be caused by an electron, and it is not a proton track. Anderson's unprecedented discovery was highly controversial until it was confirmed a year later. (Courtesy C. D. Anderson.)

When nuclei collide

In 1919, Rutherford discovered that when alpha particles from a radioactive source travel through air, a proton is sometimes produced. The alpha particles had knocked protons out of the nuclei of nitrogen atoms in the air – the first time a nuclear reaction had been observed.

Nuclear reaction experiments are no longer performed with alpha particles from radioactive sources. Large accelerators produce beams of a wide variety of particles, ranging from electrons and protons to uranium nuclei. The energy of these projectiles is very much higher than alpha particles emitted in radioactive decay and can be precisely controlled. In addition, the number of particles per second is vastly greater than a radioactive source could possibly produce. Beams of high energy particles can be directed onto targets containing any chosen nuclei, where they collide and nuclear reactions take place.

When two nuclei collide at high energies, many different processes occur, leading to the production of a variety of final products. Sometimes the resulting nuclei have a great deal of internal energy as a result of the collision. By choosing suitable beams and targets, it is possible to select what new types of nuclei will be produced in order for these to be studied. Some of these products have found a vital role in modern medicine, and many have quite different properties to the nuclei of atoms found naturally on Earth. However, as long as the energy of the incident particle is not too high, all the transmutations are consistent with the proton–neutron model: the total numbers of protons and neutrons in the products of the collision are the same as those in the original. If the energy of the collision is higher, other particles can be produced.

Carl D. Anderson, 1905–1991, discoverer of the positron. (AIP Emilio Segrè Visual Archives.)

Taking nuclei apart

One particular kind of reaction is known as photo-disintegration which, as the name suggests, involves the breaking up of nuclei by light. Just as the ultraviolet radiation in sunlight breaks up dye molecules and, in so doing, fades clothes and fine tapestries, so high energy photons can break up nuclei. These are not photons of visible light, but high energy gamma rays, the same radiation that nuclei emit when they lose energy by jumping down from one quantum energy level to another.

Just as there are machines for making high energy particles of matter, so there are machines that produce high energy gamma ray photons. However, when Chadwick and Maurice Goldhaber carried out photo-disintegration for the first time, breaking up a deuteron into a proton and a neutron, they used gamma rays from radioactivity. Today, with a machine like the one at Mainz, in Germany, it is possible to knock a proton or a neutron out of any nucleus with photons or electrons. It is easy to imagine doing this repeatedly to a nucleus, one nucleon at a time, until ending up with a deuteron, and then finally just a proton or neutron. Since it is possible to take a nucleus apart one nucleon at a time in this way it would seem that nuclei must contain only protons and neutrons. Quantum mechanics, being quantum mechanics, tells us that matters are not so simple.

Owen Chamberlain, 1920–2006, together with Emilio Segrè, discovered the antiproton, the negatively charged anti-particle of the proton, in 1955. (Copyright the Nobel Foundation.)

Something else inside nuclei

Particles can be created and destroyed, like the electrons of beta decay that are created in the decay process, or the electron–positron pairs created from high energy photons. In 1935 the Japanese physicist **Hideki Yukawa** proposed a radical, and Nobel prize winning, theory for the attractive force between nucleons. This is the force that binds a proton and a neutron into a deuteron and holds together all nuclei. Yukawa proposed that the origin of this force is an entirely new kind of particle. It is created at one of a pair of neighbouring nucleons and jumps across at near the speed of light to be absorbed by the other nucleon. It may seem surprising that this gives rise to an attractive force, but such an attraction was a clear prediction of Yukawa's calculations. There are also other examples. The electric force between charged particles (repulsive for like charges, attractive for unlike charges) is also due to exchange of particles, but in this case the particles are photons.

Yukawa's particle was eventually discovered more than a decade later, and is now known as the pion; it is the lightest of a class of particles known collectively as mesons. Originally, mesons were so-called because they were intermediate in mass between electrons and protons, the pion being about 273 times as heavy as an electron, whereas a proton has about 1835 times the mass of an electron. Over the years many other mesons have been found, including some much heavier than protons. For example the so-called B–mesons are heavier than alpha particles containing four nucleons.

According to the modern versions of Yukawa's theory, the nucleons in the nucleus are held together by mesons coming into a very brief existence during which they jump from one particle to another before vanishing again, see **Pion exchange**. The energy to create the meson is a loan from a **Quantum bank** and has to be very quickly repaid. So, at any given time nuclei must contain some mesons as well as protons and neutrons.

Mesons cannot explain everything about the force between a pair of nucleons, especially when they are very close together. A fuller understanding involves the fact that protons and neutrons, like all the mesons, are themselves composite objects. They consist of even more fundamental building blocks, called 'quarks', which are held together within the nucleons and mesons by the exchange of particles known as gluons. Modern nuclear research has opened up the whole question of how nuclei can provide a new window into Nature at the quark–gluon level.

No simple answer

When very high energy projectiles collide with other nuclei, they sometimes apparently knock pions out. However, this is not strictly evidence that there

Hideki Yukawa, 1907–1981, put forward a theory for the force that holds protons and neutrons together based on the exchange of a new kind of particle, the meson. The first meson to be discovered is now known as a pion. Yukawa received the Nobel prize in physics in 1949. (AIP Emilio Segrè Visual Archives, W. F. Meggers Collection.)

Quantum bank

Nature allows energy to be borrowed briefly to allow an exchange meson to be created out of nothing. The law of energy conservation can be challenged only for a VERY brief period; the bigger the energy loan, the more quickly it must be paid back.

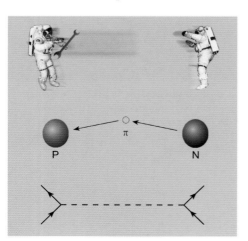

Pion exchange

If two astronauts in space were to throw spanners to each other, it would tend to force them apart. Nucleons are not like this. The reason why particle exchange causes attraction lies in the depths of the mathematics. The bottom section, with the dashed line indicating the exchanged meson, shows the diagram invented by Feynman that symbolizes the exchange process.

Jlab

An aerial view of the Thomas Jefferson National Laboratory in Virginia, USA. In the upper half and to the left is shown the above-ground buildings associated with the CEBAF and its large oval underground beam tube through which the electrons pass many times as they are accelerated. The three grassy mounds below are above the three experimental halls where the scattered particles are analysed.

are pions inside nuclei since pions can also be created out of the energy of the incident projectile. As has been seen previously, the fact that particle 'X' comes out of nuclei is not proof that nuclei have particle 'X' inside them. There are, however, some rather difficult experiments involving beams of electrons and photons which can only be understood if it is assumed that there are pions within nuclei.

It is quite typical of the quantum world that the answer you get to any question depends on how you ask it. If you ask what is in the nucleus, and ask the question with low energy particles, then the answer is: just protons and neutrons; in such a low energy experiment if a nucleus is taken apart nucleon by nucleon, nothing will be left over, certainly not a pion. Asking the question with high energy particles, the answer will be different and will include a whole variety of other particles.

Mesons do not end the list of what might be in nuclei. To introduce the new particles, we first recall that atomic nuclei, like atoms, have excited states. If a nucleus is in one of its excited states, it will quickly lose its excess energy by emitting a series of gamma rays until it reaches the state with the least energy, the ground state. In the 1950s it was found that protons and neutrons can

Producing new particles

Whe two nuclei collide at 89% of the speed of light, many particles are released. This picture, taken using a drift chamber at GSI in Darmstadt, Germany, allows them to be identified. Two of them are exotic: a K-zero particle and a lambda. They did not exist in the incoming nuclei, and very quickly decay into more familiar particles. Such experiments yield vital clues concerning neutron stars and supernova explosions (courtesy GSI).

Particles leave tracks

Tracks left by high energy particles in a bubble chamber. Some particles are bent much more easily by a magnetic field than others, just as in the diagram from Marie Curie's thesis on page 55 . A little to the left of the centre, a 'V' shows a particle–antiparticle pair created from a neutral particle that has left no track. (CERN) also be excited to higher energy states whereby their properties are changed and they become new particles. These are also possible occupants of nuclei. In **Producing new particles** we show a variety of new particles produced when two nuclei collide at high energy.

Much that we know about the many new particles was found by measuring the tracks that they left in bubble chambers, see **Particles leave tracks**. These tracks might remind you of the cloud chamber tracks shown in Chapter 3, and the principle is much the same.

The most common state that an excited nucleon can be in is known as a 'delta resonance', or a *delta*. Outside nuclei, deltas live for a very short time (about the time it takes for light to cross from one side of a proton to the other), but inside a nucleus, a proton can take a very short-term loan of energy from the same mysterious quantum bank that provides energy for mesons. Protons and neutrons use this energy to fund a brief transformation into delta particles. The result is that the proton within a deuteron is actually a delta for around one percent of the time.

It is possible to knock deltas out of a deuteron, but only by hitting the deuteron with enough energy to turn a nucleon into a delta. But only the pions from their rapid decay are detected by instruments. This is not evidence that there are deltas ready-formed inside deuterons. The evidence for deltas is either indirect or due to the fact that certain nuclear theories depend for their success on deltas, and other types of particles, being formed from excited states of the nucleon, and existing fleetingly in nuclei.

The deltas and other new particles require very large machines to produce them. Such a machine is the CEBAF electron accelerator at the Thomas Jefferson National Laboratory, widely known as **Jlab**. Electrons accelerated in this machine reach more than 99.9999% of the speed of light, allowing us to study nuclei right down to the quarks within each nucleon, and throwing light on the way nucleons interact with each other at extremely short distances. Einstein's special relativity is at work in Jlab: new particles are created in the target nuclei from the immense energy of the accelerated electrons. Theories of how a nucleus holds together can be tested by studying the way these new particles behave.

Within Hall A

This photograph shows the beam tube that carries the electrons onto the target, emerging from the concrete shielding surrounding the accelerator.

At **Jlab**, electrons in a stream with the thickness of a human hair are accelerated by electromagnetic fields in a long vacuum tube in the form of a huge underground racetrack. This can be seen in the top half of the picture of Jlab. The electrons surf the crests of intense radio waves which continually boost their energy as they are guided around the racetrack by magnetic fields. They travel more than a kilometre each lap and they make many laps, reaching almost the speed of light very quickly. After acceleration, the electrons are directed into one of the three underground target areas where the collisions take place and are analysed. These target areas, known as Hall A, Hall B, and Hall C, are beneath the three grassy mounds seen toward the bottom of the aerial photograph of Jlab. Many different particles are produced and studied in these target areas.

In Chapter 4, we saw that in order to 'see' the finest details of nuclei, particles with extremely short wavelengths are needed. The high energy of the electrons makes the Jlab machine one of the largest 'nuclear microscopes'. **Within Hall A** shows a beam tube emerging from the massive concrete shielding, carrying the high energy electrons towards the collision target. The other equipment will measure the nature and energies of the particles scattered or produced, and how many appear at each angle. This Jlab setup seems a far cry from the experiments of Geiger and Marsden from which Rutherford deduced the nuclear structure of atoms, but the core idea is the same.

Nuclear matter at high energies

We have seen that ordinary nuclei contain not only protons and neutrons but also mesons and other particles which exist very briefly before disappearing altogether when the nuclei are dismantled with low energy reactions. Examining reactions at high energies is also important because there are locations in the Universe where nuclei, or the matter of which nuclei are composed, exist in extraordinary states. Neutron stars, for example, are composed of nuclear matter, but not quite the same type of nuclear matter as the ingredients of ordinary nuclei in their ground states. The stuff of neutron stars cannot be made on Earth, but clues about it can be gained from the study of what happens when very high energy nuclei collide. Not surprisingly, many new particles are created.

When two complex nuclei collide at high energy, many different kinds of mesons besides pions emerge, and these give clues as to the behaviour of nuclear matter at high energy and pressure. This information is needed by physicists who are trying to understand neutron stars and the processes that take place in supernovae, the explosions of stars which are the source of many of the elements found on Earth.

There does not appear to be a limit to the variety of particles that can be made to come out of nuclei if enough energy is pumped in. The vast array of particles which emerge in the highest energy collisions has recently provided evidence that in very hot nuclei the individual protons and neutrons melt away leaving a soup of quarks and gluons, the so-called 'quark–gluon plasma'. It is important to understand this state of matter since conditions in the very early Universe were once fleetingly extreme enough for it to exist. In **A new state of matter?** we can see the shower of particles produced in attempts at CERN, around the year 2000, to produce a quark–gluon plasma. We return to this subject in chapter 10, describing recent results at RHIC in the USA and at the LHC at CERN.

Quantum tunnelling

The suggestion that whatever comes out of nuclei must be inside them has already been shown not to be true for electrons. The question of whether this is true for alpha particles reveals, yet again, that the quantum world makes the answer (both yes and no) extremely intriguing. Alpha particles are tightly bound nuclei with their two protons and two neutrons fitting together very snugly. It is for this reason that they often have an independent existence, of a sort, within many nuclei.

The nucleus of ^{20}Ne, the isotope of neon composed of ten protons and ten neutrons, has a structure similar to five alpha particles. This is predicted even by models which assume the twenty nucleons move freely throughout the nucleus. Although the nucleons within certain nuclei do tend to group themselves into alpha-like clusters, the clusters do not consist of four particular nucleons, or always the same four nucleons. In quantum mechanics, every proton in the nucleus is partly in every alpha-like cluster and the same is true for every neutron. The fact that all protons are identical in the special quantum mechanical sense means that every proton is equally part of every cluster. Thus the simple intuitive picture of alpha particles bouncing around in nuclei, each with its own unique set of nucleons, is not quite accurate.

A heavy nucleus like the uranium isotope ^{238}U, which decays by emitting alpha particles, has many more neutrons (146) than protons (92). It cannot be thought of as a collection of alpha particles. Nevertheless, alpha particle-like structures do occur in the nucleus and sooner or later these appear outside the nucleus as alpha particles, and can be picked up in detectors. The greater the probability that the alpha particles are emitted, the shorter the half-life of the nucleus. The half-life of a nucleus such as ^{238}U is determined by two factors. The first is the likelihood that the protons and neutrons arrange themselves into structures that look like a nucleus of the thorium isotope ^{234}Th, plus a single alpha particle. The second factor is how rapidly the alpha particle can tunnel out of the nucleus.

In 1928 George Gamow, and at the same time Gurney and Condon, see page 43, calculated the tunnelling probability of an alpha particle. It is the way that the rate of alpha particle tunnelling varies that determines the huge range of half-lives from nucleus to nucleus. For example, the half life is 4.5 billion years for ^{238}U and a third of a microsecond for the polonium isotope ^{212}Po. The essential point of quantum mechanical tunnelling is that quantum theory makes it possible for particles to tunnel through a barrier which it does not have enough energy to jump over. Such a barrier would be absolutely impenetrable according to pre-quantum physics, see **Quantum tunnelling**.

The ease with which a particle gets through this barrier depends extremely sensitively on the amount of energy possessed by the particle. Just how sensitively can be seen from the huge difference in the half-lives of the uranium and polonium isotopes. The vast ratio of half-lives corresponds to a factor of just two in energy: the alpha particle emitted by ^{212}Po has about twice the energy of the alpha particle emitted by ^{238}U. Gamow's quantum tunnelling theory gave a stunning account of how the half-life for alpha decay is related to the energy of the alpha particles. It was his theory of alpha decay that first convinced scientists that quantum theory applied to nuclei. After all, a radically new theory, quantum theory, was required to describe the properties of atoms, so it was conceivable that another, entirely new, theory was required to describe the ten thousand times smaller nuclei. Today all our understanding of nuclei is based on quantum theory.

The importance of quantum tunnelling in nuclear physics extends far beyond understanding alpha decay. The fusion reactions by which stars get their energy and by which elements are built up from hydrogen, depend on tunnelling inwards through otherwise impenetrable barriers. The sensitivity of the rate of tunnelling to the energy of the particles is a crucial ingredient in governing the rate at which stars burn and evolve. Tunnelling makes possible the generation of energy by the Sun and stars, and is the key to producing the elements from which we are made.

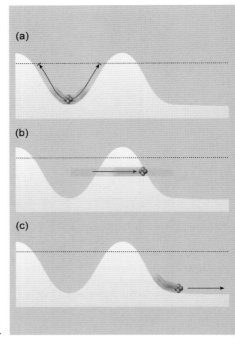

Quantum tunnelling

(a) shows a particle (imagine a marble) rolling back and forth simply does not have enough energy to get out of the well. However, quantum mechanics allows something amazing to happen: a particle with too little energy to get over the top can occasionally tunnel through the well (b) in a way that has no parallel in the world of human-sized objects. After tunnelling through, the particle accelerates 'down the hill' just as everyday experience would suggest (c).

6. The nuclear landscape

The varieties of nuclei and their varied abundances

It is obvious, just by looking around, that some elements are much more abundant on Earth than others. There is far more iron than gold, for example if it were the other way round, both the ship-building and jewellery businesses would be very different. In addition, it is not just on Earth that some elements are rare. Astronomers have found there is far more iron than gold throughout the Universe, although even iron is relatively rare since it, along with all other elements apart from hydrogen and helium, comprise just 2% of all the visible matter in the entire observable Universe. The other 98% is about three-quarters hydrogen and one quarter helium.

The tiny proportion of 'everything else' is not uniformly distributed in the Universe. Instead, it is concentrated in particular places, such as on planet Earth. The distribution of elements is also very uneven. Fortunately, Earth has a sufficient quantity of elements such as carbon, oxygen and iron, to make life possible.

It seems that some kinds of atoms have scored much higher in Nature's popularity stakes than others. What is it about carbon or iron that makes them favoured by Nature in this way, and gold so rare? These questions can now be answered by bringing together knowledge from nuclear physics, astrophysics and cosmology, see **Galaxies at the edge of the observable universe.**

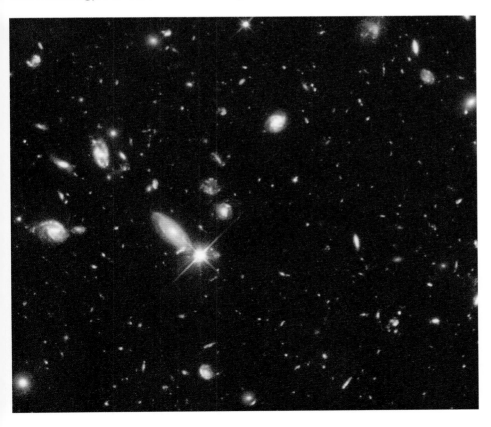

Galaxies at the edge of the observable Universe

Seen by the Hubble Space Telescope. Their light has taken billions of years to arrive so we see these galaxies as they were billions of years ago. They have had billions of years less nuclear processing than our own Galaxy and therefore contain fewer heavy elements. (NASA/STScI)

Nuclei for life

The hydrogen nucleus usually comprises just a single proton, but it occasionally has one or even two additional neutrons, but never more. This limiting factor on the number of neutrons any nucleus can contain has a profound influence on the world of matter. If a nucleus of hydrogen had one proton and 99 neutrons, it would have very strange physical properties – for instance, water made with this isotope would be solid at room temperatures.

The carbon compounds upon which life depends would be quite different if ^{40}C rather than ^{12}C were the most common isotope of carbon; the fats in our bodies would weigh about three times as much and, even more dramatically, we would have great difficulty breathing out solid carbon dioxide! But ^{40}C does not, and cannot, exist. The key to understanding what nuclei can exist lies in the energy stored within nuclei. Not only does this energy provide clues as to why certain nuclei are found in abundance and others are rare, but it also explains how energy is extracted from nuclei, both in the stars and on Earth.

What nuclei can exist ?

Nuclei can be classified into two types: stable and radioactive. A stable nucleus lasts forever, but a radioactive one is unstable and decays into a different species. If it decays into another unstable nucleus, then that will also decay. Radioactive decay will continue until a stable nucleus is formed.

There are many more kinds of radioactive nuclei than stable ones as you can see from the **Segrè Chart**. Some nuclei that have too many neutrons to be stable experience the kind of beta decay in which a neutron turns into a proton, emitting an electron and a ghostly anti-neutrino (see the left side of **Reaching stability**). Nuclei with too few neutrons for stability undergo the other kind of beta decay in which a proton turns into a neutron. All the

Deuterium: Hydrogen with an extra neutron in its nucleus is called deuterium, ^2H, and its nucleus is called a deuteron. With two extra nucleons we get tritium, ^3H, with a nucleus called a triton. Tritium beta decays to the rare isotope of helium, ^3He. Deuterium, also called heavy hydrogen, is used a moderator in some nuclear power plants, see Chapter 7.

Segrè chart

The presently known nuclei displayed according to proton number Z on the vertical scale, and neutron number N on the horizontal scale. The black squares denote the stable nuclei, and also the extremely long lived nuclei like ^{238}U that exist on Earth. The blue squares indicate nuclei with an excess of neutrons and so beta decay by emitting electrons. The red squares indicate nuclei which undergo positron decay (or electron capture). The yellow nuclei are those which decay by emitting alpha particles and the green nuclei undergo spontaneous fission. There are a few orange nuclei along the upper edge of the coloured area; these decay by emitting protons. The squares at the top right are recently produced super-heavy nuclei. This sort of diagram is called a Segrè chart.

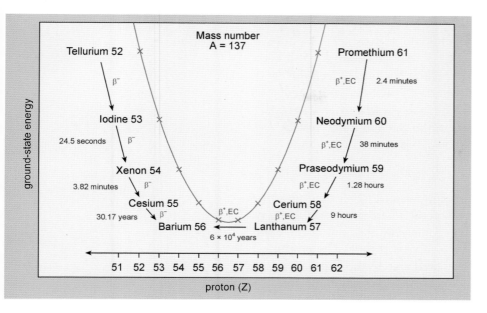

Mass number
A = 137

ground-state energy

Tellurium 52 ✕

β⁻

Iodine 53 ✕

24.5 seconds   β⁻

Xenon 54 ✕

3.82 minutes   β⁻

Cesium 55 ✕

30.17 years   β⁻

Barium 56 ←

6×10^4 years

Promethium 61 ✕

β⁺,EC   2.4 minutes

Neodymium 60 ✕

β⁺,EC   38 minutes

Praseodymium 59 ✕

β⁺,EC   1.28 hours

Cerium 58 ✕

β⁺,EC   9 hours

β⁺,EC   Lanthanum 57

β⁺,EC

51 52 53 54 55 56 57 58 59 60 61 62

proton (Z)

Reaching stability

The unstable nuclei, those indicated with red or blue squares in the previous diagram, have the wrong proportion of protons and neutrons. They correct this by beta decaying to another nucleus with the same atomic mass number. The wrong balance of protons and neutrons gives the nucleus too much energy. This energy is carried off by the electron or positron and the neutrinos. This process of losing excess energy is rather like falling down a hill and this diagram shows how the energy increases rapidly away from the stable nucleus, in this case the barium isotope ^{137}Ba (the 56 indicates that barium is the element with 56 protons). This picture shows how the energies of series of nuclei, all with 137 nucleons, form a shape known as a parabola. The nuclei up the sides of the parabola eventually lose energy, falling down to the bottom in a series of beta decays. The half-lives for the decays are shown.

possible stable nuclei have been known for many years, but the tally of known radioactive nuclei is continuously expanding. New and interesting radioactive nuclei are regularly produced in laboratories, with properties that challenge our theories of nuclear structure. These exotic nuclei play a crucial role in various key processes in which elements, such as the lead in our car batteries, are made in stars. Many of them are very unstable, having half-lives much less than a second. Some survive for such a brief period that they can hardly be said to exist at all, yet their fleeting existence in stars has left its mark on the world around us.

It is not yet known exactly how many neutrons can exist in a nucleus with a given number of protons before it becomes so unstable that it effectively does not exist. This is an active field of theoretical and experimental research, and at present we cannot predict the total number of possible nuclei.

Our theories of nuclear structure have been guided by the patterns of which nuclei are stable. For example, the nuclei of most elements up to calcium, with an atomic number, Z, of 20, have a handful of different isotopes, and in each case there is always a stable isotope with either the same number of neutrons as protons, or one additional neutron. The elements with an odd number of protons generally have fewer isotopes than elements with an even number. Fluorine, sodium and aluminium (with Z = 9, 11 and 13), for example, have just one isotope each, while oxygen, neon and magnesium (with Z = 8, 10 and 12), each have three isotopes.

For elements up to calcium, stable isotopes have similar numbers of protons and neutrons. From calcium onwards there is a change, and stable isotopes exist with more neutrons than protons, calcium itself having a rare isotope ^{48}Ca. The most common isotope of calcium, ^{40}Ca, with 20 neutrons, is the last stable nucleus having an equal number of protons and neutrons. For heavier elements, stable nuclei contain more neutrons than protons and the excess of neutrons increases with atomic number. For example, there are stable isotopes of lead, which has 82 protons, that contain 122, 124, 125 or 126 neutrons. The most common uranium isotope, ^{238}U, has 92 protons and 146 neutrons; thus if you add 10 protons, you must also add 20 neutrons.

Some nuclei are not completely stable, but have long enough half-lives to be found naturally on Earth. Examples are the uranium isotope ^{238}U and the potassium isotope ^{40}K. The small amount of ^{40}K that we all have in our bodies makes us slightly radioactive, with some 15 million ^{40}K nuclei decaying every hour in each of us. This radioactivity contributes to the background radiation that we all experience. Half of all the ^{238}U that was present when the Earth was formed, 4.5 billion years ago, still exists in the soil and rocks. In fact, ^{238}U is much more common on Earth than gold, which is a stable element.

The driplines

There are some nuclei that take even more drastic steps to get their proton–neutron balance right – they emit protons directly. These nuclei, on the very edge of stability, lie along the 'proton dripline', marking the limit of the number of protons a nucleus can have, even for a very short time. The proton dripline is near the left hand edge of the coloured area in the **Segrè chart**, and the orange dots mark the proton-emitting nuclei. Similarly, the neutron dripline marks the limiting number of neutrons a nucleus can hold without them being emitted immediately. At the time of writing the neutron dripline has only been reached for some of the lightest nuclei, up to about $Z=14$, silicon. The maximum possible number of neutrons is not yet known for nuclei with more than 14 protons. The neutron dripline is some way off to the right of the coloured zone in the **Segrè chart**. For nuclei with more than 60 protons, there are other forms of radioactivity. Some decay by emitting alpha particles while others undergo spontaneous fission: they split, without any prompting, into two, approximately equal, lighter nuclei. This process has had momentous implications for humans and also, together with alpha decay, puts a limit on the total number of protons and neutrons that a nucleus can have.

The energy valley

Generally, the greater the imbalance of protons and neutrons in a nucleus, the shorter its half-life. When a nucleus undergoes beta decay, the emitted electron and neutrino carry off energy. The energy lost in this way is nearly always larger for decays between pairs of nuclei that are highly unstable. The more energy that is lost by the nucleus, the more rapidly the emission takes place and thus the shorter the half-life.

Among nuclei with a certain number of nucleons, the stable nuclei have the least energy while unstable nuclei have excess energy, which they lose by transforming themselves through beta decay. The more unstable the nucleus, the more excess energy it possesses. It is as if the stable nuclei are at the bottom of a valley with the height above the valley floor being a measure of the energy stored in the nucleus. Nuclear physicists refer to this as the valley of stability. Continuing the valley analogy, nuclei with more energy are like boulders perched up the side of the valley; they are less stable than ones at the bottom – a nudge could send them rolling down. Not only does the valley slope upwards, but it also gets steeper further from the bottom. This is why beta decay, in which nuclei lose energy by jumping down the sides of the valley, greater. Boulders lying at the bottom of the valley need to have energy supplied to them to lift them up the side of the valley. In **Reaching stability,** we see how all nuclei with $A=137$ roll down the slopes by beta decay to end up as ^{137}Ba.

Along the valley floor

The amount of energy stored in a nucleus depends on the total number of protons and neutrons (the atomic mass number A) as well as on the proportion of protons to neutrons. The more protons and neutrons in a nucleus, the more energy it has. The important quantity is really the energy per nucleon. This is just the total energy divided by A.

If we make a graph of the energy per nucleon of all the nuclei that, like ^{137}Ba, have the lowest energy for a given mass number, we get what we see in **The most stable nuclei**. The energy per nucleon is high for very low A, reaches a minimum near $A=60$ and then slowly rises for large A. This is a very important diagram, and much about how energy is released by processes in the Sun as well as nuclear reactors can be explained using it, as we shall see.

When all known nuclei are placed in a single figure, in which the height represents the energy per nucleon, we get the energy valley shown in **The energy valley**, in which the bottom of the valley traces out a path like the line in **The most stable nuclei**. The sides of the valley are like what we have seen for $A=137$. The stable nuclei all lie along the floor of a valley which is not level, but slopes toward a lowest point that is near particular nuclei with 26 or 28 protons. These nuclei have less energy per nucleon than any other nuclei. The bottom of the valley itself slopes upward slowly in the direction of the heaviest nuclei such as uranium and more steeply toward the lightest nuclei.

Element 26 is iron, and the position of the nuclei of certain isotopes of iron near the bottom of the valley is one reason why iron is very abundant both on Earth (the central core of the Earth is largely iron) and in the rest of the Solar System. Once the nuclei of iron are formed within stars, they are reluctant to transform into anything else without further energy being supplied. Elements with more protons than iron or nickel (element 28) tend to be less abundant on Earth and in the stars than most of the lighter elements such as carbon and oxygen. This is due largely to the way elements are made in stars, but the energy valley is also a key factor.

In a similar manner to a river flowing along a valley floor towards the lowest point, the lightest atomic nuclei undergoing reactions tend to move towards the region near iron where the energy is lowest, by acquiring more protons and neutrons. Heavy nuclei can also move towards the lowest region by somehow transforming themselves into nuclei with fewer protons and neutrons. Thus two very different processes are involved, depending on the direction of the flow: *nuclear fusion* for light nuclei and *nuclear fission* for heavy nuclei.

Nuclear fusion and fission

If two very light nuclei can be made to coalesce or 'fuse' into one heavier nucleus, energy will be released because the heavier nucleus has less energy per nucleon than the lighter ones. Energy will therefore be 'left over' after the nuclei have coalesced. This is nuclear fusion, and is the source of the energy from the Sun. Most of this comes from hydrogen fusing to form helium. Fusion reactions that produce energy cannot produce nuclei heavier than iron or nickel, the nuclei at the lowest point of the valley.

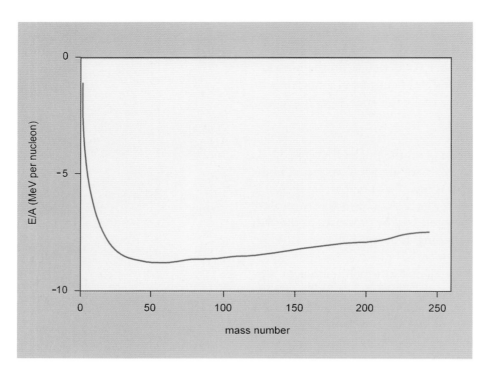

The most stable nuclei

The total energy of a nucleus is not exactly proportional to the mass number, A , the number of nucleons. This graph shows how the energy per nucleon, written E/A, depends on A. The most stable nuclei are those near the lowest point on the curve, around mass number 56 to 60. Both the lightest nuclei and the heaviest nuclei have more energy for each nucleon than the nuclei with about 60 nucleons. That is why energy is released when the lightest nuclei undergo fusion to make heavier nuclei, or the heaviest nuclei undergo fission and split into two lighter nuclei. On this graph, the energy is that of the most stable nuclei with that particular mass number A, in other words the nucleus near the bottom of the parabola in the previous figure **Reaching stability**.

The energy valley

How the energy of a nucleus depends on Z, the number of protons, and N, the number of neutrons. The grey surface is in the form of a valley and the height represents the energy per nucleon, E/A. The valley floor follows the shape of the the curve on the previous figure, and the sides of the valley curve upwards as shown for mass number 137 in the figure before that. This figure also shows grooves or 'gullies' crossing the valley — these show the way the energy dips down for the magic numbers. The black pillars are there to guide the eye to the red lines which indicate the magic numbers. One gully crosses the valley for proton number 50, and another for neutron number 82.

In stars hotter and more massive than the Sun, other fusion processes occur. When a magnesium nucleus with 12 protons fuses with a silicon nucleus with 14 protons to make an iron nucleus with 26 protons, a great deal of energy is released. Much of the iron in our Solar System was probably made in processes like this when massive stars exploded about five four billion years ago.

The valley floor sloping upwards from iron in the direction of the heaviest nuclei means the amount of energy per nucleon is getting progressively greater. If a heavy nucleus splits into two, the resultant, lighter nuclei would exist lower down the energy valley and each would have less energy per nucleon. The total amount of energy contained by the resultant nuclei is less than the energy of the original nucleus. Therefore, after the split there would be some surplus energy. Such nuclear splitting is known as nuclear fission. When a heavy nucleus undergoes fission, the surplus energy is released mostly in the energy of motion of the two lighter fragments as they fly apart.

Fission is the source of much of the electrical energy used by many nations and it is the source of the man-made element, technetium, used to treat cancer and other diseases. In addition it forms the basis of weapons of dreadful destruction.

One of Nature's greatest surprises

The discovery of nuclear fission in the late 1930s came as a huge surprise. There was nothing in the behaviour of atoms to suggest that their nuclei should behave in such a way. Ernest Rutherford, and all the other nuclear pioneers, had given up hope that the energy locked within nuclei could be extracted and harnessed. Then, Otto Hahn and Fritz Strassmann were astonished to discover that when uranium was bombarded with slow neutrons, traces appeared of the much lighter element, barium. They worked hard to convince themselves that it really was barium produced, and not radium, an element with similar chemical properties but much closer to uranium in mass.

With hindsight, it might seem obvious that a uranium nucleus had split into two fragments, one of these being a barium nucleus, but this was initially far from obvious. It was only some months later, while on a skiing holiday in Kungälv in Sweden, that **Lise Meitner** and her nephew **Otto Robert Frisch** came up with the now accepted picture of nuclei undergoing what they called fission – the word used by biologists for the process by which living cells divide, see **The discovery of nuclear fission**. Frisch soon observed that the barium nuclei flew off at high speed, carrying away a lot of energy. The energy of nuclei could, after all, be extracted and maybe put to use.

When a nucleus undergoes fission, the two lighter nuclei that fly apart are soon slowed down by nearby atoms, to which some of the energy is transferred. In this way, a great deal of heat is generated which can be made to turn water into steam, powering turbines that generate electricity – but there is an unfortunate consequence. Consider, once more, the bottom of the energy valley. For heavier nuclei, the stable isotopes contain more neutrons than protons, thus the floor of the valley curves away from the diagonal line that represents nuclei with equal numbers of protons and neutrons. If, for example, the uranium isotope ^{235}U absorbs a neutron, the resulting ^{236}U will undergo fission. It can split in a variety of ways, but will often split into nuclei of barium and krypton. These might be ^{146}Ba and ^{90}Kr; since barium has $Z=56$ and

Lise Meitner, 1878–1968. Born in Vienna, she worked for many years in Berlin doing research in radioactivity. Element 109, meitnerium, is named after her. (AIP Emilio Segrè Visual Archives.)

Otto Robert Frisch and Lise Meitner spent their winter holidays together in the boarding house on the right. The Swedish sign (above) says "Lise Meitner and her Nephew Otto Frisch formulated here an explanation of the discovery of the splitting of the uranium nucleus."

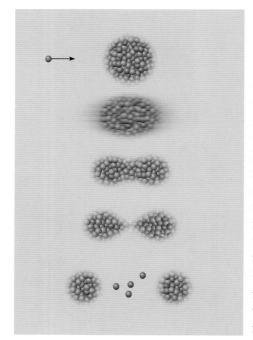

The discovery of nuclear fission

Meitner and her nephew Otto Robert Frisch, 1904–1979, were the first to recognize a certain phenomenon discovered by Hahn and Strassmann as a signature of nuclear fission, the process shown above. An incoming neutron is absorbed by a uranium nucleus which becomes "excited" and splits in two. A number of fresh neutrons are also released. Their fission model was based on Niels Bohr's 'liquid drop' model of nuclei, and predicted that fission releases much energy. At that time, in 1939, Meitner was taking refuge in Sweden.

krypton has $Z=36$, the number of protons adds up to 92 – the correct Z for uranium. In addition, the total number of nucleons adds up to 236.

The problem is that the heaviest stable barium nucleus is ^{138}Ba and the heaviest stable krypton nucleus is ^{86}Kr, so both of the nuclei that are produced in fission have a large excess of neutrons. This means they are positioned somewhere up the side of the energy valley, an unstable state from which they will inevitably tumble down in a chain of beta decay steps. Hence, due to the curve in the energy valley, nuclei produced in fission will always be somewhere high up the neutron-rich side of the valley. The nuclei produced in nuclear fission are therefore highly radioactive. Some of these radioactive nuclei have a long half-life, casting a shadow over the application of nuclear fission for nuclear power. In fact, the fission products of a splitting uranium nucleus will not be quite so far up the valley walls as the example above suggests. When a nucleus divides in two, not all of its neutrons go into the two lighter nuclei. A few, generally two or three, are released. These can then be absorbed by other ^{235}U nuclei, turning them into fissionable ^{236}U. This is of great importance, making nuclear fission a practical source of energy, because these neutrons will then induce more uranium nuclei to split. These in turn release more neutrons, each of which would cause more uranium nuclei to fission, and so on. This is the famous fission chain reaction and is illustrated in **The discovery of nuclear fission.**

When the chain reaction takes place in a slow and controlled way, we have nuclear reactors that can produce electricity and isotopes for medical purposes. When it happens rapidly, in an uncontrolled way, we have a nuclear bomb.

Limitations of mass

In about 1942 it was found that uranium nuclei can, very occasionally, undergo fission without any stimulation by neutrons. This process is called spontaneous fission and helps answer the question of which nuclei can exist.

Spontaneous fission becomes more and more important for the very heaviest nuclei, and is one of the factors that determines just how heavy a nucleus can be. The nuclei for which spontaneous fission is the dominant mode of decay are coloured green in the **Segrè chart** and in **Nuclear limits**.

At the top end of the valley of stability, most nuclei decay by emitting alpha particles. Alpha particle decay can also be thought of as a kind of fission in which one of the nuclei produced is very much smaller than the other. Energy is released, and carried off by the alpha particle, in a similar manner to when a nucleus undergoes fission. The resulting nucleus lies further down the energy valley than the original one and, although the alpha particle itself is far down at the other end of the valley floor, it is also a very stable nucleus. The tendency for nuclei to alpha decay is also a major limiting factor to how heavy nuclei can be. As we saw in Chapter 5, the half-life of a nucleus undergoing alpha decay is exceptionally sensitive to the energy of the alpha particle: the more energy carried off by the alpha particle, the shorter the half-life. Thus the excess energies of the alphas at the extreme top end of the valley indicate that these nuclei are very short-lived.

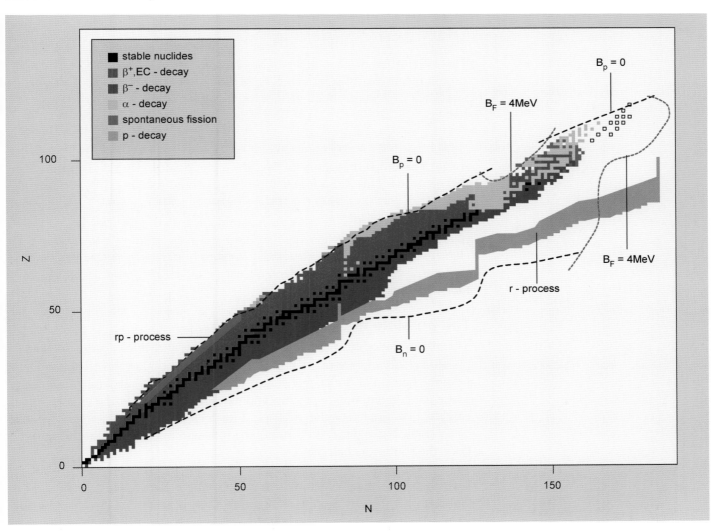

Nuclear limits

When viewed on a Segrè chart like this, the possible nuclei do not extend indefinitely in all directions. The limits are called the 'driplines' and are shown in this figure. For example, add a neutron to a nucleus on the neutron dripline (B_n=0), and it would 'drip' right out again since the neutron binding energy, B_n is zero here. Apart from the lightest nuclei, we do not get near the neutron dripline. We do reach the proton dripline (B_p=0) in some places. The possibility of spontaneous fission also imposes a limit on which nuclei can exist; the green line marks this limit. Beyond it, nuclei are expected to live so fleetingly that they can hardly be said to exist. Later on we explain the r-process (pink areas) and the rp-process (green).

Magic numbers

So far, the energy valley has been presented as being smooth, but studied more closely, it is seen to be rather bumpy. This is because the energy per nucleon of stable nuclei does not follow a smooth curve. A select few are slightly lower than their neighbours since they have even less energy per nucleon (more stable). Such nuclei tend to line up together in grooves that criss-cross the valley floor. These grooves occur for particular numbers of protons and neutrons known as magic numbers. A good example occurs with the series of nuclei lying on the line for 50 protons. The isotopes of the element with $Z=50$, tin, have somewhat lower energy per nucleon than their neighbours, and have various other properties that are associated with greater stability. Tin also has more stable isotopes (10 in all) than any other element.

The number 50 is also significant for neutrons. All the nuclei on the line signifying 50 neutrons have a little less energy per nucleon than their neighbours. Thus a nucleus with either 50 protons or 50 neutrons will be significantly more stable than nuclei with slightly fewer, or more, protons or neutrons. Although they are not deep compared to the main energy valley itself, these grooves have a profound effect on what nuclei exist, and also contain vital clues about the structure of nuclei.

There are other magic numbers. The complete set is: 2, 8, 20, 28, 50, 82 and 126. In recent years, experiments have shown that the influence of magic numbers can become much weaker for nuclei far up the sides of the valley of stability.

Nuclei that have magic numbers of both protons and neutrons are especially stable. The simplest example is ^{4}He, the alpha particle, with two protons and two neutrons. This is the reason for its exceptional stability. Another example is the isotope of lead, ^{208}Pb, with 82 protons and 126 neutrons. Lead is common on Earth, and ^{208}Pb is its most abundant isotope. However, lead is surrounded by quite rare elements that have relatively unstable nuclei. The next element after lead is bismuth, $Z=83$, which is hundreds of times rarer than lead in the Earth's crust. All elements with more than 83 protons only have radioactive isotopes.

The possible nuclei

The energy valley answers some questions about what nuclei exist; for example, it explains why there are no ^{40}C or ^{100}H nuclei – they would lie too far from the bottom of the energy valley. The existence of a nucleus containing a particular combination of protons and neutrons depends on the energy of the combination. Some combinations yield nuclei that last forever, others are subject to radioactive decay. In general, the further a nucleus is from the valley floor, the shorter its half-life.

There is a limit to how high we can go above the valley floor; go beyond a certain point and any protons or neutrons that we might try to add to a nucleus leak right out again. These limiting points mark the boundaries of the region where nuclei either exist or would exist if we could make them. These boundaries are the driplines shown in **Nuclear limits**. In some places we do know where they are, and in other places we can make informed guesses. In **Nuclear limits**, the dashed lines mark the probable driplines as explained in

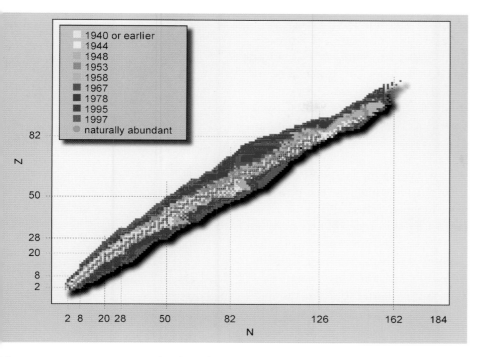

Nuclear discovery

Every discovery of new nuclei has revealed new phenomena to challenge theory. The need to understand nuclear processes in stars makes it even more urgent to push further into the unknown, since many nuclei near the neutron dripline play key roles in the processes that form the heavy elements. Here we see how active this adventure into dripline territory has been in recent years.

the captions. We are very far from having reached the neutron dripline at present. **Nuclear limits** shows that there are many nuclei that must exist but which have not yet been identified in the laboratory. The number of nuclei that have been created and studied increases year by year, as can be seen from **Nuclear discovery** which shows how far we had reached by 1997.

The super-heavies

Although all the isotopes of thorium, $Z=90$, and uranium, $Z=92$, are strictly unstable, both elements have one or two isotopes with extremely long half-lives – as long as the age of the Earth in the case of uranium, and three times longer than that for thorium. All isotopes of elements with more than 92 protons are much too short-lived to have survived since the Solar System was formed. It naturally became an irresistible challenge to make nuclei with more than 92 protons using nuclear reactions! These are known as the transuranic nuclei since they have more protons than uranium.

An early cyclotron

One of the first large cyclotrons at the Lawrence Radiation Laboratory, Berkeley, 1944. From left, Luis Alvarez, William Coolidge, William Brobek, Donald Cooksey, Edwin McMillan and Ernest Lawrence. Alvarez and Lawrence were later awarded Nobel prizes in Physics, Lawrence for inventing the cyclotron and Alvarez for discovering many new particles using bubble chambers. McMillan, discoverer of element 93, neptunium, shared a Nobel prize in chemistry with Glenn Seaborg for their work on transuranic elements. McMillan later helped develop the synchrotron, the high energy successor to the cyclotron. (Berkeley National Laboratory, AIP Emilio Segrè Visual Archives.)

Element 93, neptunium, was identified by Edwin McMillan and Philip Abelson in Berkeley, California, in 1940 using early cyclotrons, see **An early cyclotron** and **Making a new element**. Over the years, elements 94 (plutonium) to 103 (lawrencium) were also produced at Berkeley as a result of heroic efforts by **Glenn Seaborg**, Albert Ghiorso and their large team using cyclotrons and other accelerators. Elements 104 (rutherfordium) to 107 were for many years the subject of claims by workers at Berkeley and at Dubna in Russia.

Advances in making new elements are currently being made at GSI near Darmstadt in Germany, and in Dubna in Russia. The challenge the physicists face is formidable. As the number of protons increases, the half-lives of these elements gets shorter. For example, the longest lived isotope of rutherfordium, ^{263}Rf, has a half-life of about ten minutes. Alpha decay and spontaneous fission compete to make nuclei of the other isotopes vanish even more quickly. Moving up to element 107, half-lives are typically measured in seconds or milliseconds. Nuclei with higher Z are progressively harder to make and live ever more fleeting existences.

Glenn Seaborg, 1912–1999, discoverer of plutonium and other elements. Element 106, seaborgium, is named after him.

For many years, nuclear theory has suggested that 114 is a new magic number for protons. This might lead to an 'island of stability' around elements 112 or 114, where lifetimes are longer than expected and perhaps become long enough for the chemical properties of the elements to be studied. The term 'island' is a little misleading since it implies a higher level than its surroundings – in the picture of the energy valley, these more stable heavy nuclei would actually reside in a lower energy region than their surroundings. It is not yet clear whether this island of super-heavy nuclei exists.

The curvature of the energy valley adds to the difficulty of making superheavy nuclei. It dictates that the heavier the nucleus, the greater the excess of neutrons over protons, but super-heavy nuclei must necessarily be made using reactions with lighter nuclei, having a smaller ratio of neutrons to protons. It follows that the nuclei made in these reactions will have too few neutrons to be near the bottom of the energy valley. To make the job even harder, these heavy nuclei undergo fission with little prompting, and the very reactions in which they are made are likely to put a lot of energy into the system. Too much energy would nudge any nucleus with a tendency to fission to take the plunge and break up again.

Even if a few super-heavy nuclei are made, identifying them is extremely hard. Finding a needle in a haystack is nothing compared with having to identify the single super-heavy nucleus produced per day when trillions of particles are hitting the detectors every second. The efforts to study these exotic nuclei are very rewarding to both physicists and chemists; chemists can check whether they can predict the chemical properties of hitherto unknown elements, while physicists have an invaluable test of their theories, which predict the probability of alpha decay and spontaneous fission.

Step by step the GSI physicists have worked their way up through new elements with shorter and shorter half-lives. These include element 109, meitnerium (named after Lise Meitner), identified in 1982, and elements 110 darmstatium, 111 roentgenium discovered in 1996, and 112 copernicium discovered in 1996. The main developments in superheavy research are at the GSI near Darmstadt in Germany and at the Flerov Laboratory of Nuclear

Reactions, JINR, in Dubna, Russia. The current state of play is shown in the table. Before elements are named there must first be an internationally agreed confirmation; in the meantime, they are referred to by temporary names such as Ununquadium, which just means one-one-four-ium.

In June 2011, an international committee, applying stringent criteria, agreed that elements 114 and 116 really had been made, but as this book goes to print, their names have not yet been agreed.

Man-made elements past uranium.

Z	Name	Symbol	Place	Year	Uses and applications
93	Neptunium	Np	USA	1940	Instruments for detecting neutrons
94	Plutonium	Pu	USA	1940	Power, weapons, power for spacecraft.
95	Americium	Am	USA	1944	Smoke detectors, industrial gamma source
96	Curium	Cm	USA	1944	Alpha source; detects elements on Mars
97	Berkelium	Bk	USA	1949	None known
98	Californium	Cf	USA	1950	Portable neutron source for industry
99	Einsteinium	Es	USA	1952	There is too little of this for use.
100	Fermium	Fm	USA	1952	Ditto
101	Mendelevium	Md	USA	1955	
102	Nobelium	No	USA	1958	
103	Lawrencium	Lr	USA	1961	
104	Rutherfordium	Rf	USA	1964	
105	Dubnium	Db	Russia	1967	
106	Seaborgium	Sg	USA	1974	
107	Bohrium	Bh	Germany	1981	
108	Hassium	Hs	Germany	1984	
109	Meitnerium	Mt	Germany	1982	
110	Darmstatium	Ds	Germany	1994	
111	Roentgenium	Rg	Germany	1996	
112	Copernicium	Cn	Germany	1996	
113	Not named	Uut	Russia/USA	2004	
114	Not named	Uuq	Russia	1998	
115	Not confirmed	Uup	Russia	2004	
116	Not named	Uuh	Russia	2000	
117	Not named	Uus	Russia	2010	
118	Not named	Uuo	Russia	2006	

Exotic nuclei at the driplines

Great efforts are being made to extend our knowledge of nuclei in the directions of the lowest and highest possible neutron numbers for a given Z – the most neutron-rich and neutron-deficient isotopes of an element. Such unstable nuclei are hard to make on Earth, but they do exist briefly when stars explode. They are created en route to producing many of the elements on Earth, including some of those inside our bodies. We can never fully understand where the elements on Earth come from, or the stars they were made in, without studying the exotic, highly unstable nuclei closely.

Exotic nuclei are also very interesting because many of them are so unlike the more familiar stable nuclei. Examples are the halo nuclei ^{6}He and ^{11}Li, which are much larger than the stable isotopes of helium and lithium. Understanding these weird nuclei has proved to be a great challenge to both theorists and experimentalists. Theories can be adjusted to explain all the known stable nuclei quite well, but the real test is whether they can predict the properties of these new exotic nuclei.

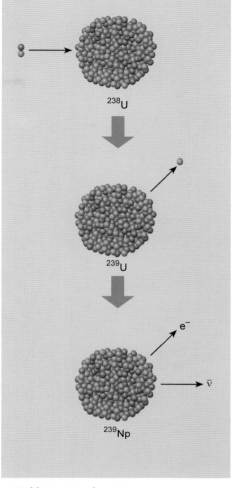

Making a new element

McMillan and Abelson made neptunium by bombarding ^{238}U with deuterons. There is a good chance that the neutron in the deuteron will be absorbed while the proton continues on its way. In that case ^{239}U will be formed. However ^{239}U has too many neutrons for stability and beta decays emitting an electron and anti-neutrino within minutes to form ^{239}Np.

The most stable nucleus

Iron makes up most of the Earth's core due to its exceptional stability. It is also one of the most common elements in the Solar System and is near to the lowest point in the energy valley. It is therefore natural to think that there must be a connection, and there is, but, as always when dealing with Nature, there are complications. In fact, the most common isotope of iron, ^{56}Fe, is not quite at the lowest point in the energy valley. That privilege goes to an isotope of nickel, ^{62}Ni, the most stable nucleus in nature. However, it is not nearly as abundant in the Solar System as ^{56}Fe. The reason is simple: a nucleus not only has to be as stable as possible, but there must also be an efficient pathway for its production from other nuclei.

A full account of why some nuclei are abundant and others are rare must take into account both how stable the nucleus is, and the mechanisms by which it can be produced. The iron isotope, ^{56}Fe, is produced by fusion of lighter nuclei in certain very hot exploding stars. It turns out that there are no nuclei in these stars that could then fuse with ^{56}Fe to make ^{62}Ni.

Thus, the rarity of gold is not only a matter of its position on the energy valley, but also a consequence of the rarity in the Universe of the processes that make it. The reason carbon is more abundant than gold is partly because the stellar processes that make ^{12}C occur on a widespread scale in the Universe.

7. Applications of nuclear physics

Interactions with everyday life

By the 1930s, nuclear physics was entering a golden age. Almost all the elements were known and their chemical properties established: from hydrogen with its nucleus consisting of just one proton, to uranium with 92 protons and well over a hundred neutrons. There remained just a few conspicuous gaps in the periodic table – apparently, elements with certain atomic numbers simply did not exist on Earth. Nuclear physicists have since artificially created and identified the nuclei of these elements; one, in particular, has turned out to play a vital role in modern medicine and has also become of great significance to astronomers.

The element in question has atomic number 43 and was discovered in 1937. In that year Ernest Lawrence used his new particle accelerator, the cyclotron, to send a beam of deuterons onto a target containing element 42, molybdenum. When the deuterons, the nuclei of an isotope of hydrogen containing just a proton and a neutron bound together, interacted with the molybdenum nuclei, reactions took place making the target radioactive. Some deuterons deposited their neutron in the molybdenum target nuclei, while their proton continued on its way; the extra neutron in these molybdenum nuclei caused them to become unstable and suffer beta decay, with a neutron becoming a proton accompanied by the emission of an electron and an anti-neutrino. In this manner, element 42 becomes element 43.

Emilio Segrè, 1905–1989, shared the 1959 Nobel prize in physics with Owen Chamberlain for the discovery of the anti-proton. He had many other discoveries to his credit, including new elements. (AIP Emilio Segrè Visual Archives)

Lawrence did not study the molybdenum targets himself – he sent them off to a promising young student of Fermi, **Emilio Segrè**, who had just taken up a post in Palermo, Sicily. Segrè and his colleague, Carlo Perrier, analysed the targets and found traces of a hitherto unknown element which they succeeded in identifying as the missing element 43. Later, they called this element technetium, since it was the first element produced by artificial, or 'technological' means. It was given the symbol Tc and a gap in the table of the elements was filled.

No one had found technetium on Earth because it has no stable isotopes. Even the longest-lived isotope has a half-life of just over four million years – short enough for any amount of technetium originally present on Earth when the Solar System was formed to have decayed away.

Subsequently a number of other missing elements – 61 (promethium), 85 (astatine) and 87 (francium) – were also produced using nuclear reactions, but it is technetium which has become deeply significant to the lives of many thousands of people. As an example of its importance, when the world supply of technetium was threatened by a strike at a nuclear laboratory in Canada in 1998, the President of the American College of Nuclear Physicians wrote a strongly worded letter to the Canadian Prime Minister pointing out that 47,000 medical procedures per day, in the USA alone, were under threat. In addition, medical procedures throughout the world were being cancelled. Currently, some 30 million medical-imaging procedures involving technetium are carried out every year. The technetium story is one example of how human exploration of the heart of matter has led to discoveries which have become part of everyday life. Modern medicine and modern industry would be untenable without them.

Detecting and measuring radiation

Before exploring how radioactive elements are used in medicine and industry, we must examine what happens when radiation passes through matter and how it is detected and measured.

The key to all the effects of radiation – useful and life saving, as well as damaging and life threatening – is its power to ionize the material through which it passes. The process of ionization means that electrons are knocked out of atoms and molecules, leaving them electrically charged. Alpha, beta and gamma rays are all examples of ionizing radiation. As an alpha particle, for

A real photomultiplier tube has about 10 dynodes, and about a million electrons reach the anode for each electron ejected from the photocathode.

Detecting gamma rays by scintillation

A common means of detecting gamma rays and measuring their energy relies on scintillations, the flashes of light given off as gamma ray photons interact with suitable substances. A common choice is a crystal of sodium iodide, NaI, doped with about 1% of thallium. A gamma ray disturbs the electrons of many atoms (one is shown here) and each atom emits photons of visible light as it settles down. The higher the energy of the gamma ray, the more photons are emitted. By measuring the intensity of the flash, the energy of the gamma ray can be measured. Photons comprising the flash are guided to a photomultiplier where they release electrons from a photocathode into a vacuum tube containing a series of dynodes. The electrons are accelerated from dynode to dynode by an electric field, and each time they strike a dynode more electrons join the stream, ending up at the anode where they enter an electronic measuring circuit. The whole system is called a gamma ray spectrometer. Germanium detectors, like those shown in Chapter 4, are used when the energy of the gamma ray photon needs to be measured with great precision, as in certain nuclear physics experiments. Similarly, silicon detectors, like those shown in Chapter 3, are used for detecting charged particles when the energy and direction of the particle must be measured precisely. Semiconductors like silicon and germanium give an electrical signal when struck by a photon or changed particle.

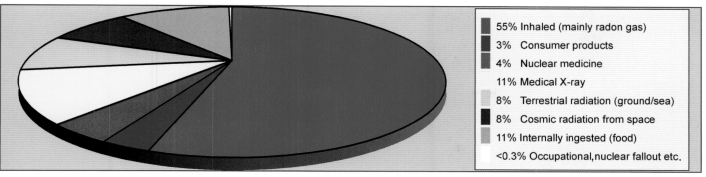

Sources of background radiation

55% Inhaled (mainly radon gas)
3% Consumer products
4% Nuclear medicine
11% Medical X-ray
8% Terrestrial radiation (ground/sea)
8% Cosmic radiation from space
11% Internally ingested (food)
<0.3% Occupational, nuclear fallout etc.

The proportion of radiation we receive from different sources varies at different locations. This chart shows the average for the United States, as published by the National Council for Radiological Protection.

instance, passes through matter, it knocks electrons out of many atoms and molecules in its path, leaving a trail of free electrons. The displaced electrons are damaging to life, disrupting DNA in cells, for example, possibly causing mutations and even killing the cells. As it leaves a trail of ionization through matter, the alpha particle will steadily lose energy and slow down until it eventually comes to rest. We shall see that it is important for medical applications that the ionization is greatest just before it comes to rest.

Gamma rays and X-rays also ionize the material they pass through. They eventually disappear by being absorbed by the atoms, rather than losing energy by slowing down. The interaction of gamma rays with matter makes it possible for them to to be detected and their energy measured, see **Detecting gamma rays by scintillation**. As they are forms of electromagnetic radiation, there is only one possible speed for X-ray and gamma ray photons: the speed of light.

All forms of ionizing radiation have a range beyond which they are effectively fully absorbed. This range depends on the energy and the nature of the material; lead, for example, is more effective than most materials at stopping radiation and is therefore used for shielding. Neutrons are an exception in this respect. Being neutral, neutrons are most strongly absorbed by substances containing much hydrogen, such as water or paraffin. This is because the neutrons lose energy by making the light protons in water or paraffin recoil, thus absorbing the energy of the neutron.

Natural and artificial radiation

Natural radiation is all around us. Over the history of life on Earth, living creatures have evolved senses which warn of dangers such as excessive temperature and approaching predators, but humans, at least, have no sense that responds rapidly to ionizing radiation. We are quite unaware of any variation in the radiation to which we are subjected. Natural sources of radiation include the ground we walk on, the air we breathe and the food we eat. Some naturally occurring radioactive isotopes, such as uranium and thorium, are left over from the time when the Earth was formed – others, such as the carbon isotope ^{14}C, and tritium, ^{3}H, are made by interactions within the atmosphere when high energy particles (cosmic rays) bombard the Earth from space, see **Sources of background radiation**.

One of the most abundant radioactive isotopes found on Earth is that of potassium, ^{40}K, which makes its way into the food chain. It exists as small traces alongside the stable isotope, ^{39}K, which is vital for life. Once ingested, the traces of ^{40}K slowly decay inside our bodies but most will be excreted. Another radioactive element absorbed by humans is ^{14}C. All living organisms take in carbon, which contains a constant fraction of radioactive ^{14}C. Once an organism dies and stops taking in carbon, the amount of ^{14}C can be used to determine the time elapsed since death. This is the basis of carbon dating. The largest amount of natural radiation to which humans are exposed is by breathing in the noble gas, radon. Radon, atomic number $Z=86$, is a decay product of uranium found in rocks. It is chemically inactive, allowing it to migrate through porous materials such as house foundations. Once in the air inside the house it can be breathed in, where it has a chance of decaying inside the lungs.

The amount of radiation we receive depends on the kind of rocks in the ground beneath us, how high we live above sea level and, in recent times, what sort of job we do. Dentists giving X-rays to their patients, or miners working underground in certain kinds of rock, will receive extra radiation. Airline crews who spend more time than most at high altitudes also receive extra radiation from the effects of cosmic rays. The natural background radiation varies a great deal, and is usually much greater than man-made radiation.

We all experience some man-made ionizing radiation – from minute amounts emitted by smoke detectors to sometimes quite substantial doses encountered in medical treatments. Many people have jobs involving low levels of radiation and we also receive radiation from the nuclear power industry. While these sources are usually very much smaller than the background, the Chernobyl and Fukushima incidents serve as a warning that this powerful force must be treated with respect.

Nuclear physics in medicine

Everybody will know of someone who has benefited directly from applications of nuclear physics in medicine. Some measure of its importance can be judged from the monetary figures: worldwide; already by the year 2000, nuclear medicine was a $10 billion per year business. In Europe and the US, radioisotopes are used in some way in the treatment of almost half of all hospital patients.

Nuclear medicine is important for both diagnosis and therapy. Diagnosis ranges from routine use of X-rays to injection of radioactive material for gamma imaging, while the best-known use of radiation for treating disease is radiotherapy used against cancer. The power of radiation to cure is often less publicized than its power to do harm – radiation as invisible scalpel rather than invisible dagger. Just as a scalpel must be wielded with extreme care, so radiation must be carefully controlled. Doctors who prescribe such radiotherapy must weigh the risks of radiation against the benefit of the treatment.

The effect of radiation on living tissue does not just depend on how much energy is deposited, but also on the type of particles involved. When a gamma ray interacts with the nucleus of a cell, one half of the double strand of the genetic material DNA might be broken, but there is a good chance that the cell will repair itself. When an alpha particle passes through a cell, the much more intense trail of ionization is more likely to destroy both strands, something the cell cannot repair. Fortunately, alpha particles have a short range, and will not pass through human skin; unfortunately, there are some sources of alpha particles, such as radon gas, which can enter the body just from the air we breathe. However, extensive surveys in the US and UK have found virtually no correlation between environmental radon levels and disease, which illustrates the adaptive power of living organisms.

There are two reasons why radiation from radioactive nuclei and high energy particles from accelerators are powerful weapons against disease. Firstly, radiation preferentially destroys fast growing tissues such as cancers. Secondly, radiation can be concentrated in the specific tissues which need to be destroyed. This is particularly true for beams of protons and heavier nuclei. As we shall see, such particles give up most of their energy at the end of their path so that it is possible to arrange for the dose to be delivered to a well-defined volume within the patient's body.

Before a medical condition can be treated, it must be detected and a diagnosis made. Many gamma-emitting radioisotopes, such as technetium, can be used as 'tracers'. Wherever a tracer goes in the body it can be followed by suitable detectors that measure its characteristic radiation. It can be made into a chemical form that concentrates in particular organs, allowing the precise location, shape and biochemical function of those organs to be mapped out. This is something X-rays cannot do with soft tissue.

The particular form of technetium used as a tracer is called ^{99m}Tc, or technetium-99m. This is an excited state of the isotope of technetium with 56 neutrons as well as the 43 protons. The 'm' (for metastable) indicates a very unusual property – it is an 'isomer', a long-lived excited state. Nuclei, like all quantum systems, have excited states that decay to states of lower energy, usually giving off the energy difference as gamma rays (photons). Normally, the photons are emitted within billionths of a second of the nuclear state being produced, but there are a few cases where they are delayed. Such a case is ^{99m}Tc in which the delay is quite long, with a half-life of six hours. This is helpful in that the ^{99m}Tc does not emit gamma rays for long within the patient. Moreover, the gamma ray is readily detectable outside the patient.

In addition to technetium, the radioisotopes of a number of other elements such as cobalt, copper, caesium and iodine, are crucial in medicine. Others, such as phosphorus, calcium, chromium, selenium, strontium and xenon, have uses in biomedical research to study anything from metabolism to bone formation and cell function.

An important application of radioactive tracers in medicine is positron emission tomography (more commonly known as PET). When compounds containing short-lived isotopes such as ^{11}C, or ^{13}N are injected into a patient, they can be followed as they concentrate in particular organs. This is possible because they emit positrons as they decay and these particles very quickly encounter their anti-particles, electrons. When this happens, the two particles rapidly annihilate each other and two energetic photons are emitted in precisely opposite directions. By detecting such pairs of photons, with sub-microsecond timing, the place in the body where an ^{11}C or ^{13}N nucleus has decayed can be determined quite accurately. By detecting many such pairs over a period of time, the detailed changes in concentrations of key biological chemicals can be mapped out. The functioning of living hearts, brains and

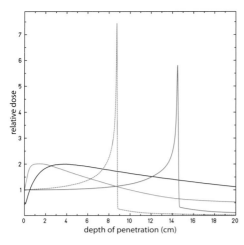

Bragg peak

Gamma-ray and X-ray photons give up their energy to the medium they pass through very differently to the way charged ions give up their energy. The black line shows that X-rays from a powerful source, as used for treating cancer, release much of their energy soon after entering the body, with a gradual fall-off with depth of penetration. The green line shows that gamma rays from a ^{60}Co radioactive source behave in a somewhat similar way. However, high-energy ^{12}C ions release most of their energy just before coming to rest at a sharply defined depth; this is represented by the sharp rise known as the Bragg peak. The depth of the peak depends on the energy, with the dashed red line corresponding to ^{12}C ions having a somewhat lower energy than those corresponding to the solid red line.

Heavy ions or protons

Both protons (black line) and ^{12}C ions (red line) deposit their energy towards the end of their path through matter, but the Bragg peak is much more sharply defined for the heavy ions. This enables ^{12}C beams to be designed so that the ionization is almost completely confined within the tumour.

other organs can be studied and their diseases diagnosed. Brain damage suffered in a stroke, for example, can be mapped out precisely. PET has also become an important method for understanding the normal function of the brain and other organs.

Some medical isotopes, such as technetium, are now produced in specialized variants of nuclear power reactors, whereas others are produced by nuclear reactions using small cyclotrons. Many hospitals have their own cyclotrons for making certain radioactive isotopes, especially the positron emitters used for PET, which live much too briefly to be transported to the hospital.

Fighting cancer with protons and heavy ions

We mentioned that beams of protons and heavier nuclei give up most of their energy near the end of their paths. This is illustrated in **Bragg Peak**, which contrasts with the way X-rays deposit energy. From **Bragg Peak**, you see that X-rays deposit more energy where they enter the body. It has long been realized that this is not an ideal situation when using X-rays to destroy cancers. The question is: can we use beams of protons and heavier nuclei, like those used in nuclear physics experiments, to destroy cancer tumours? Would it be possible to adjust the beam so that the Bragg peak, where the beam dumps most of its energy, lies within the tumour itself? Might it even be possible to trace out the volume of the cancer within the delicate organs that would be damaged by too much radiation?

The answer is yes. Physicists have developed ways of adapting the techniques, which were originally developed for studying collisions between nuclei, to the treatment of certain kinds of cancer. The practicality of using beams of high energy protons and, more recently, heavier nuclei such as ^{12}C, has been studied and applied in many countries, with ^{12}C proving particularly useful. In particular, techniques extensively developed at the GSI nuclear physics laboratory in Darmstadt, Germany, are being put into practice at the Heidelberg Ion-Beam Therapy Centre. They plan to treat 1300 patients in 2011.

Proton beams have been used for treating cancer for some time in various places around the world. So why go to the trouble of accelerating ^{12}C ions to very high energies? The answer is suggested by **Heavy ions or protons**. It is evident that the Bragg peak is much narrower for ^{12}C ions than for protons. This makes it possible to dose even a very odd-shaped tumour while sparing the healthy tissue. There is also a bonus with ^{12}C ions: some of the ^{12}C ions undergo a nuclear reaction forming the nucleus ^{11}C, a positron emitter, allowing the radiation of the tumour to be monitored using PET, positron emission tomography, described in this chapter.

The treatment of cancer with beams of ^{12}C ions was pioneered using the huge patricle accelerator at the GSI nuclear physics laboratory near Darmstadt in Germany. It is not surprising that clinical treatment requires a very large accelerator too like that of the **Heidelberg Ion-Beam Therapy Centre** (HIT) which developed out of GSI research. The **HIT Gantry** allows the beam to be directed precisely where it is needed.

1. IONENQUELLEN
2. LINEARBESCHLEUNIGER
3. SYNCHROTRON
4. HOCHENERGIE-STRAHLTRANSPORT
5. HORIZONTALBESTRAHLPLÄTZE
6. DIGITALES RÖNTGEN
7. GANTRY
8. GANTRYBESTRAHLPLATZ

Heidelberg Ion-Beam Therapy Centre

The scale of the Centre can be judged from the size of the figures undergoing treatment in this diagram. The 'race track' at the top left is the synchrotron, around which the ions go many times as they are accelerated to near the speed of light. The ions are guided by magnets through vacuum beam tubes to the treatment areas. The large blue structure on the right is the gantry that allows the beam to be directed at any angle to the patient. By adjusting the energy as the beam is moved, it is possible for the Bragg peak to trace out the precise volume of the tumour.

HIT gantry

A photograph of the blue gantry see schematically in the **Heidelberg Ion-Beam Therapy Centre.**

Nuclear power

The process of nuclear fission releases a tremendous amount of energy and during the second half of the 20th century many countries developed the technology to harness this energy to produce electricity. Nuclear reactors currently supply 16% of the world's electric power. In these reactors, the energy is provided by the fission of uranium into two or more pieces, releasing a tremendous amount of heat in the process. The same kind of reaction also generates the explosive energy of an atomic bomb; but whereas in an atomic bomb the energy is released all at once, in a reactor the energy is released at a controlled rate. As an illustration of how effective nuclear energy can be, the total fission of one kilogram of uranium releases as much heat as a million kilograms of coal. However, commercial reactors 'burn' only a few percent of the fresh uranium fuel placed in them; the rest must be reprocessed chemically before it can be used again.

Naturally occurring uranium consists almost entirely of the isotope ^{238}U with less than one percent of ^{235}U. It is, however, only this rare isotope that will undergo fission in an ordinary nuclear reactor, and there is only so much economically recoverable uranium ore in the Earth's crust. The most common type of reactor operates with 'enriched' uranium, which consists of a few percent of ^{235}U, but this mix is not capable of sustaining a chain reaction on its own. Reactors therefore use a moderator such as water or graphite to slow down the neutrons that are released during fission to make them much more likely to initiate further fission reactions. The heat produced in the reactor is then used to produce steam that drives turbines, which in turn produce electricity.

In a breeder reactor, the abundant ^{238}U can be converted into an isotope of plutonium, ^{239}Pu, which provides an alternative fissionable material to ^{235}U. This is accomplished when neutrons released in the fission process convert a little of the uranium into plutonium. Such reactors therefore produce new fuel as well as energy.

Nuclear fission contributes a considerable fraction of the developed world's current energy requirements. In so doing, it replaces the burning of fossil fuels (coal and oil) that appear to be the cause of damaging global climate changes resulting from CO_2 emissions. Already, nuclear fission contributes over half the electrical power requirements of some countries, for example France. However, of understandable concern to the public is the fact that it yields highly radioactive waste that has to be confined and stored safely for many years. There is hope, however; a number of practicable solutions which involve transforming this waste into a far less harmful state are under development.

There are several alternative approaches that might tackle the waste problem. A number of countries are considering ways of developing a revolutionary type of reactor that would either incinerate or transmute the radioactive waste products. One idea, for a hybrid reactor has been around since the early 1990s when initial studies were carried out at Los Alamos in the US and CERN in Switzerland. It involves connecting up a high energy proton accelerator to a sub-critical nuclear reactor (one in which there are not enough neutrons to sustain a chain reaction). The protons collide with a nuclear target producing neutrons which are then used to incinerate the long-lived waste products by transforming them into nuclei that are far less radioactive and have shorter half-lives. The intention is that the final products of this process would be no more harmful than the natural uranium that was originally mined from the ground. Finding a satisfactory solution to this problem may yet make nuclear energy an ecologically sound alternative to fossil fuels before the environment is irretrievably damaged.

Industrial, environmental and domestic applications

Radioactive isotopes, or simply 'radioisotopes', are used throughout industry. Often they are a source of penetrating gamma rays that can be used, rather like super X-rays, for examining such things as ball bearings and jet turbine blades for flaws. Just as radioactive tracers allow particular chemicals to be followed through the human body, so there are a vast number of applications of tracer techniques in industry, biological sciences, and in monitoring pollution in the environment.

The inventor of tracer techniques, George de Hevesy, even applied the method to restaurant evaluation. He had heard rumours that steak left by customers in his favourite restaurant was reused at a later date in ground, or minced, form. He injected some mildly radioactive isotope in a steak and left it on his plate. The next day, the ground beef that he ordered set the Geiger counter clicking; a classic application of tracers back in the 1930s!

Many radioisotopes that are routinely used today in a wide range of industrial applications belong to elements that are not well known. The elements americium, cesium and curium, for example, are vital to the mining industry to help decide where to drill oil wells. Americium is probably best known for its use in domestic smoke detectors, see **Americium in every home**, but it is also used to measure levels of toxic lead in paints. Other radioisotopes used in industry include cadmium, which is used for sorting scrap metals and analysing alloys; californium,

Americium in every home

The key to the operation of a smoke detector is a tiny amount of americium isotope, ^{241}Am, a by-product of nuclear reactors. The alpha particles from the americium ionize the air which then conducts a tiny electric current between two electrodes. When smoke penetrates the space between the electrodes, the particles remove the ions which conduct the current, the current is reduced, and the alarm is triggered.

which is used to inspect airline luggage for hidden explosives; and krypton, which is used in the indicator lights of many household appliances from washing machines to coffee makers. In addition, tritium, the isotope of hydrogen with two neutrons (as compared with deuterium which has one), is used to make self-luminous signs and paint, and has been used in wrist watches for the same purpose.

There are many nuclear reactors that have been designed specifically for making isotopes, for industrial or scientific research, or for teaching. The beautiful blue glow of a reactor using water as a moderator can be seen in **A 'swimming pool' research reactor**.

Even uranium isotopes have many uses, such as in dental fixtures and wall tiles, while an isotope of plutonium, ^{238}Pu, with a half-life of 88 years, has safely powered many spacecraft since 1972 including the Cassini-Huygens mission that reached Saturn in 2004, see **Powering Cassini**.

Nuclear physics in astronomy

Almost everything we see when we look up into the night sky is the result of nuclear reactions. Stars shine because nuclear reactions are taking place at their centres, but their nuclear fuel does not last forever. The detection of the short-lived element technetium in stars which are billions of years old proved that such elements are created within them.

As nuclear fusion processes turn hydrogen into heavier elements, generating heat, stars undergo a series of changes at a rate which depends on their mass. The heaviest burn their nuclear fuel very quickly before exploding as supernovae. Lower mass stars like the Sun will, after shining for a few billion years, expand and cool. During this stage they are known as 'red giants', and when the Sun becomes one, its outer atmosphere will swallow the Earth.

Red giants also played a vital part in our history. The Solar System condensed out of gases and dust that was enriched by cinders from exploding stars and by material thrown off by an earlier generation of red giants. Many of the heavy elements existing on Earth, like the lead on our roofs, were produced by these red giants in the 's-process' which allows heavy elements to be formed by the slow addition of neutrons. These processes are described in detail in Chapter 9. Certain man-made elements past uranium have played a crucial part in study-

Powering Cassini

The Cassini spacecraft, launched in 1997, took seven-years to reach Saturn and its moons, and is still, in 2011, returning data. In late 2010, Cassini provided images of torrential methane rain on Saturn's moon Titan. The electrical power for the on-board equipment comes from energy released by the decay of radioactive nuclei. The plutonium isotope ^{238}Pu in the form of plutonium oxide releases enough heat for the 'Radioisotope Thermoelectric Generators' (RTGs) to produce 870 watts of electrical power. (Courtesy ESA.)

ing the surface of Mars, as explained in **From medicine to Mars**. On page 93 we show **Sojourner** on the surface of Mars, and in particularon the **APXS** (alpha proton X-ray spectrometer) which uses the curium isotope ^{244}Cm.

Radioactivity and the history of the Earth

The Earth and the rest of the solar system were formed about 4.6 billion years ago out of interstellar material ejected by exploding stars. Amongst those primordial atoms were some that were radioactive, uranium, for example. Those radioactive atoms are important for us, and not just as a possible source of energy. They help answer basic questions about the history of our world. For example, just how do we know that the solar system is some 4.6 billion years old? You may have read that some particular rocks were 500 million years old; how do we know? That question deserves an answer.

A key means of measuring the age of old rocks, and even the Earth itself, is through *radiometric dating*. This is based on the fact that each kind of radioactive nucleus decays in a regular and predictable way. In Chapter 3 we saw that each particular kind of nucleus has its own half-life, the time in which just one half of a collection of such nuclei decay. Half-lives vary enormously from one kind of nucleus to the other, but they can be billions of years. It is from certain long-lived nuclei that were present when the Earth was formed that we can learn about the long history of the Earth. For example, ^{238}U has a half life 4.5 billion years, so that just about half of the original ^{238}U nuclei will have decayed by now. What they decay into carries a message. When a ^{238}U nucleus decays, an alpha particle is emitted and a thorium nucleus ^{234}Th appears. The alpha particle quickly picks up electrons to become a helium atom. The accumulating helium is locked away in the uranium ore when the ore finally solidifies. That is how Lord Rutherford was able to say by about 1905 that he knew the ages of certain rocks in his pocket. His idea was to heat the rock and measure the helium that was released. Of course, he had to take into account how much uranium was still in the rock, and the rate at which it decayed.

Rutherford's ideas were soon developed by Bertram Boltwood and others. Since that time radiometric dating has advanced enormously, and many techniques have been developed. For example, the ^{234}Th itself will decay, and so on through a chain of short-lived nuclei until we finally reach the stable nucleus ^{206}Pb, an isotope of lead. But ^{206}Pb is not the most common lead isotope, the most common being ^{208}Pb, and ^{207}Pb is almost as common as ^{206}Pb. The normal proportions of the different lead isotope were determined when most of the lead on Earth was expelled from aging stars. But sometimes an anomalous amount of ^{206}Pb is found in minerals otherwise poor in lead, but containing uranium. Careful measurements of the amounts of ^{206}Pb and ^{238}U yield a remarkably accurate date at which the mineral crystallized. Uranium also provides a dating scheme for somewhat younger rocks. The rarer ^{235}U isotope decays much more rapidly than ^{238}U, with a half-life of 'only' 700 million years, ending up as the lead isotope, ^{207}Pb. Dating rocks that are thousands or millions rather than billions of years old is better done with isotopes having a shorter half-life, and there are enough of these to cover a wide range of dates. An extreme example is carbon dating, based on the decay of ^{14}C and already mentioned in this chapter. Since the half-life of ^{14}C is 5700 years, it cannot be

From medicine to Mars

What elements are present on the surface of Mars? How much carbon, or any other element, is there in a biopsy sample and how is it distributed in the sample? Questions like these arise time and again in medicine, in industry and in planetary exploration.

A very old idea, reborn with modern techniques, comes to the rescue. It harks back to the alpha particle scattering experiments which revealed to Rutherford that all atoms had central nuclei. In those experiments, alpha particles were fired at a sample and a few came straight back. Geiger and Marsden's targets were pure metals such as gold. But a sample might have many different elements in it. If so, the energy the alpha particles have when they fly back to be detected depends on the mass of the nucleus which they strike, just as a tennis ball bounces back with more energy if it hits a soccer ball rather than a ping-pong ball. So if we can measure the exact energy of each alpha particle which bounces straight back, and count how many have particular energies, we can say exactly how much of each element there is in the part of the sample we are studying. This way of studying samples is called Rutherford Backscattering Spectrometry (RBS). It was used to make the first measurements of what elements were on the Moon long before people went there. Alpha particles from an Americium, ^{241}Am, source, which was landed on the Moon, were bounced off the lunar surface. The alpha particles were then counted and sorted by energy and the numbers beamed back to Earth.

More recently, in 1997, RBS was employed by the Mars Pathfinder rover, named Sojourner, to send back to Earth information about the elements on the surface of Mars. In this case, it was part of a package of three methods which all made use of alpha particles emitted by the transuranic element Curium (^{244}Cm). The lighter elements in the rocks, like carbon and oxygen, were measured by RBS. Somewhat heavier elements, like fluorine and sulphur, were analysed by nuclear reactions in which an alpha particle is absorbed by a nucleus and knocks out a proton. By measuring the energy of the proton, the target nucleus can be identified. The third technique is called PIXE (Particle Induced X-ray Emission). When the alpha particles strike somewhat heavier atoms, such as iron, they knock electrons out of their atomic orbits. As a result, the atom emits X-rays as they settle down after the disturbance. These X-rays allow the element to be identified. Using the combined package of RBS, nuclear reactions and PIXE, Sojourner was able to send back a detailed account of what elements there were in the rocks it encountered on Mars.

RBS and PIXE working together help to answer the question: are nanoparticles dangerous for our health? For example, titanium oxide nanoparticles are widely used in cosmetics because they efficiently reflect the Sun's ultra-violet radiation. But are they safe? Do the nanoparticles remain on the skin surface or can they pass through to reach living cells? Ordinary chemical techniques can measure the concentration of any element in a sample of tissue, but only by destroying the tissue. Moreover, they don't tell us just where the elements are located within the tissue. However, when RBS and PIXE work together, they can map out where elements are localized within cells. PIXE locates the heavier elements like titanium, while RBS reveals the cell structure by measuring the lighter elements in the same sample.

PIXE uses very fine beams of nuclear particles, focused down to a few millionths of a metre. In the case shown in the two pictures below, protons imaged a layer of human skin where a sunscreen had been applied. In the left-hand picture the carbon found by RBS reveals the cells. The picture on the right shows, in colour, where the titanium is located, as revealed by PIXE using the same beam. There was too little titanium to be detected under the outermost layer of skin. Research like this suggests that nanomaterials such as titanium oxide nanoparticles, used in cosmetic preparations or sunscreens, are not a risk to human skin.

Today, RBS has a wide range of industrial applications. It is an ideal way of looking for defects in the very thin multi-layered structures found in modern micro-electronics. RBS can call upon the full range of modern nuclear physics techniques for detecting particles, measuring their energies and counting them. Particle accelerators can provide beams of whatever particle is most suitable, not just alpha particles, and direct them with great precision onto the part of the specimen to be studied.

Skin cells imaged using RBS

(left) The darkness indicates the carbon concentration. (right) The same skin with superimposed colour indicating the titanium revealed by PIXE. Both images are from the Institute for Nuclear Technology, Lisbon.

APXS

This view of Sojourner clearly shows the alpha proton X-ray spectrometer. (NASA)

Sojourner

In this view of the Martian surface seen from the Mars Pathfinder lander is the rover, named Sojourner, which was equipped with an alpha–proton–X-ray spectrometer to analyse the elements in the Martian rocks. (Courtesy NASA/JPL/Peter Smith.)

used to date material more than about 60,000 old, since after ten half-lives there is too little left to measure accurately.

The oldest rocks?

In August 2010, research was published, based on measurements of ^{206}Pb, ^{207}Pb and also ^{204}Pb, together with isotopes of helium, neodymium and hafnium, suggesting that certain rocks were almost as old as the earth: 4.5 billion years. These rocks from Baffin Island in Greenland, had been ejected from within the Earth so that, if the age is confirmed, the discovery should lead to new understanding of the Earth's interior.

Making history

Radioactive rocks not only help us to understand the history of our planet, they also help to *make* that history. One of the earliest puzzles of radioactivity, from the time of Rutherford and the Curies, is the continuous outpouring of energy from even small samples of powerfully radioactive substances like radium. Earlier in this chapter we saw that the heat from the plutonium isotope ^{238}Pu, half-life 87.7 years, powered the Cassini spacecraft. Uranium, with its very long half-life, will not feel hot when held in your hand, because only a very small proportion of the nuclei are decaying at any one time. But in a large volume like the Earth the heat can only escape very slowly. As a result, the energy released by the radioactive decay of uranium, as well as the potassium isotope ^{40}K, does make a difference: the total power is roughly that of 30,000,000,000 one-kilowatt electric radiators. This helps to maintain the temperature of the Earth's mantle (the region 2,890 km thick between the central core and the thin crust). Heat-driven convection within the mantle moves the continents —it is likely that advanced life would not have evolved without continental drift. In that case, we would not be here without radioactivity deep within the Earth.

8. Nuclear architecture
From hydrogen to neutron stars

In Chapter 6 we asked some basic questions: Which nuclei exist? Which nuclei are stable and which are radioactive? We found that a single remarkable pattern, the *energy valley*, gives general answers to such questions. From where a nucleus would sit in the valley, we can say whether it is likely to exist, whether it is likely to be stable, and if not stable, how it would decay. We can also deduce how much energy might be extracted from it. But why is there an energy valley, with just the characteristics that it has? To answer that question, we must delve into the architecture of nuclei. The structure of nuclei depends on the quantum rules that control the properties of the protons and neutrons, and the nature of the forces between them. To follow the architectural analogy, the nucleons are the bricks, and the nuclear forces provide the mortar, while everything is under the control of rigorously enforced planning regulations provided by the quantum rules.

The force between protons and neutrons

The forces that hold nuclei together are not like any in the everyday world. Nuclear forces only act over extremely short distances – distances so short, that a nucleon on one side of a heavy nucleus, such as a lead nucleus with 208 nucleons, cannot feel the presence of a nucleon on the opposite side, see **Distance counts**. The range of the force is about 2 femtometres, compared to 13 femtometres for the distance across a lead nucleus. The short range of the force between nucleons has a big influence on the shape of the energy valley.

The reason for the short range of the nuclear force can be understood in terms of the exchange of 'force carrying' particles between the two interacting nucleons. We have seen how a pion, created using borrowed energy, is exchanged between two nucleons to generate the force between them. The range has to be small since the pion can travel only a very short distance before Nature calls back the energy loan. Electric and magnetic forces have longer ranges since they result from the exchange of photons, which are massless. For photons, Nature allows an unlimited loan period.

The nuclear force is also very much stronger than the other forces in nature. This strength is partly what causes the energy bound up in nuclei to be about a million times greater than the energy holding atoms and molecules together. Consequently, about a million times more nuclear energy can be extracted from a given mass of uranium than chemical energy from the same mass of coal.

The force between a pair of nucleons is also highly complex, and this book will not examine it in depth. Its strength, for instance, depends on the way the two interacting nucleons are spinning relative to each other. It also depends on whether they are the same type of nucleon (two protons or two neutrons) or a proton and a neutron.

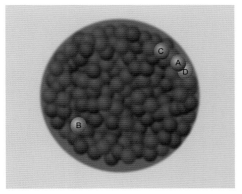

Distance counts

The force between nucleon A and nucleon C is strongly attractive. Nucleon D, however, is too close and is repelled by nucleon A, while nucleon B on the other side of the nucleus is outside the range of the force due to A.

Femtometre: 1 femtometre is 10^{-15} metres. An atom is typically 100 000 femtometres across.

The force is not quite strong enough to bind two neutrons or two protons together, but is just strong enough to bind a proton and a neutron to make a deuteron. The force between two protons is the same as the force between two neutrons except that there is also the electric repulsion between them. This electric force is, however, completely overwhelmed by the nuclear force when the protons are close together, but is significant for two protons on opposite sides of a large nucleus. Another feature of the force between two nucleons is that at very short distances, half a femtometre or so, it changes from being attractive to repulsive. As a result, two nucleons cannot overlap (under normal conditions) in a nucleus.

The nuclear force is incredibly finely balanced. A few percent stronger and two protons (or two neutrons) would bind together. Nuclei consisting of just two protons do not exist, but if they did all the hydrogen would have been consumed in the Big Bang leaving none to power ordinary stars, including the Sun. It would then have been impossible for life to evolve on Earth. If, however, the nuclear force were a few percent weaker, the deuteron would not be bound. Most of the energy from the Sun comes from a process which starts with the formation of deuterium, so if this occurred, again life would not have evolved on Earth. In either case, the elements produced in the later stages of the Big Bang would have been quite different.

Quantum rules rule

According to quantum theory, a proton or a neutron does not have a particular place in a nucleus in the same way that a brick has a fixed location in a house. Each proton and neutron has a certain probability of being found at a particular place, and that place could be anywhere within the nucleus. There are more likely and less likely places for a nucleon to be found, as determined by its *wave function*. This is the mathematical rule specifying the probability for a nucleon to be found at any particular place. It describes an orbit, a little like the orbit of electrons in atoms and not at all like the orbits followed by planets. While it is difficult to visualize electrons in their smeared out orbits around nuclei, it is even harder to imagine how nucleons might move round in the crowded nucleus. Electron scattering experiments can allow us to map out where a proton in an orbit is likely to be. The box **A proton orbit** shows that the 82nd proton in lead is quite likely to be at the centre of the nucleus and in two concentric rings further from the nuclear centre.

A proton orbit

This very sharp peak from electron scattering experiments shows that the 82nd proton in lead is most likely to be found near the centre of the nucleus. The outer rings show that the proton can also be found at about 4 and 7 femtometres from the centre of the nucleus. In most cases, the last proton in a nucleus does not have such a large probability of being at the centre of the nucleus.

1 fm

Nucleon orbits have one dramatic property: the less spread out in space a particular orbit is, the more energy of motion (technically, the kinetic energy) the nucleon has. This is one aspect of Heisenberg's **Uncertainty Principle** and is the main reason why nuclei do not collapse to a point even though the very strong nuclear force is pulling each nucleon towards its neighbours. The fact that the nuclear force between nucleons becomes repulsive at very short distances stops the nucleus being quite a point, but without the Uncertainty Principle nuclei would definitely be much smaller.

To see how the Uncertainty Principle works, imagine trying to make a nucleus smaller. In that case, each orbit would have to be more compact simply to describe the smaller volume in which a proton is found. The Uncertainty Principle imposes a cost for this to happen: in a smaller volume, the energy of motion becomes larger, which means energy needs to be added to a nucleus to make it smaller. As a result, nuclei are highly incompressible. The actual size of a nucleus with a particular number of nucleons is a balance between the nuclear forces pulling the nucleons together and the Uncertainty Principle keeping them apart.

Two other factors work together with the Uncertainty Principle to dictate nuclear sizes. One is the repulsive part of the force that takes over when nucleons get very close to each other. The other is the quantum rule known as the Pauli Exclusion Principle. This dictates that only two protons and two neutrons can occupy each possible quantum orbit. *Two* protons (or two neutrons) are allowed because there are two possible directions of their spin angular momentum.

Every orbit must obey the Uncertainty Principle, but some orbits are more compact than others. Nucleons fall preferentially into the innermost, most compact, unfilled orbits. Adding nucleons to a nucleus progressively fills up shells, making it bigger. The nucleus grows in such a way that its central density remains close to the characteristic density for the centre of all nuclei. In this respect, nuclei are very different from atoms, which are all roughly the same size. In atoms, all the electron orbits get smaller as electrons are added. This is because an atom will only be able to accommodate more electrons if its nucleus has more protons, and this extra positive charge draws all the electron orbits inwards. There is nothing equivalent at the centre of the nucleus to pull in the nucleon orbits.

Two contrasting pictures

We have presented two quite different pictures of nuclei. On the one hand, protons and neutrons deep within a nucleus lie in orbits much as electrons in atoms do, but on the other hand nuclei behave in many ways as if they were made of incompressible fluid. All nuclei except the very lightest have much the same density, much as water droplets all have the same density. If the nucleons are so closely packed together it is hard to see how they could possibly be orbiting around inside the nucleus at the same time. Water molecules certainly do not travel in simple orbits within a water droplet.

The energy valley reflects the two contrasting aspects. In the first place it has an overall smooth structure which can be summed up in just three curved lines: the height of **The floor of the energy valley**, **The energy parabola** (below), and the bend in the line of black squares in the Segrè chart (see page 68) as N becomes greater than Z for the heavy stable nuclei. However, the

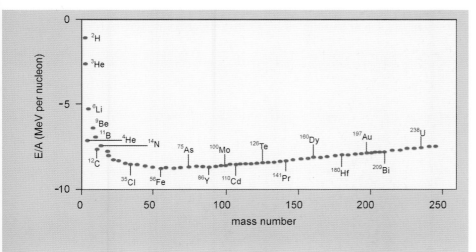

The floor of the energy valley

The floor of the energy valley showing where some particular nuclei lie. The height is the energy per nucleon, labelled E/A. It is lowest near iron (Fe), highest near the lightest nuclei such as hydrogen (H), and gradually becomes higher for elements heavier than iron. The shape of the energy valley explains why energy is released by fusion of light nuclei and by fission of heavy nuclei.

Maria Goeppert-Mayer (1906-1972) with the King of Sweden at the ceremony in 1963 when she received a share of the Nobel Prize in physics.

basically smooth valley is crossed by a number of small ditches or gullies following the lines of the magic numbers. It turns out the magic numbers are a signature that nucleons lie in quantum orbits. This was the great discovery of **Maria Goeppert-Mayer** and J. H. D. Jensen, rewarded by the Nobel prize in physics for 1963. At the time of their work, the prevailing view was that nuclei were somewhat like liquid drops, and indeed some of their properties can be explained by modelling a nucleus in that way.

Are nuclei, then, like water droplets or like miniature solar systems with nucleons in orbits? The answer is that they are not quite like either but are somewhat like both. This might seem paradoxical, but our expectations are formed by our experience with the world of visible things, and the quantum world is very different. A unified theory of nuclei, that encompassed both nucleons in shells as well as drop-like nuclear properties, was achieved in the 1950s and 1960s, with contributions from many people.

A droplet of nuclear material

Consider the way the floor of the energy valley first slopes down as we move from the lightest stable nuclei until it reaches its lowest point around iron and nickel, and then slowly rises again towards the heavy nuclei. This overall behaviour can be explained in terms of the average force felt by each nucleon, see the **Floor of the energy valley**.

The short range of the nuclear force means that in any nucleus, the nucleons in the surface 'feel' the attractive force of a smaller number of other nucleons than those deep within a nucleus. In light nuclei, a higher fraction of the nucleons are near the surface so, overall, these nuclei are less tightly bound than heavier ones, see **Neighbours attract**.

One way of expressing this is by saying that light nuclei have extra energy, called surface energy, that makes them more weakly bound. All nuclei, visualized as droplets of nuclear matter, would have the same average energy per nucleon were it not for additional effects such as the surface energy, which is largest for the lightest nuclei, making them less stable. This is reflected in the steep upward rise of the floor of the valley in the region of the lightest nuclei.

The slow increase in energy, and decrease in stability, towards the heaviest nuclei is mainly due to the electrostatic repulsion between the protons. Although the electrical force is much weaker than the nuclear force, its longer range makes it important for larger nuclei. Every proton in a nucleus feels the attractive nuclear force only of its nearest neighbours, but feels the repulsive

The energy parabola

Moving up from the bottom of the valley floor, energy increases as the proton number and neutron number change for a fixed number of nucleons, in this case 137. The proton number is shown after the name of the element, but all elements are ^{137}Te, ^{137}I, etc.

energy

proton excess   Z = N   neutron exess

Displacing the valley bottom

If there were no repulsion between protons, the energy would be lowest when the number of protons, *Z*, was the same as the number of neutrons, *N*. The most stable nuclei would have the same number of protons and neutrons as shown by the green line. This tends to be true for nuclei with less than 20 protons. Where there is a proton excess, there is additional energy, indicated by the red vertical lines. This is due to the repulsion between all the protons and is larger the greater the excess of protons. The total energy is shown by the blue line, and at its lowest point there are more neutrons than protons. This is why heavy nuclei have more neutrons than protons.

electrostatic force of every other proton in the nucleus. This repulsion therefore builds up as the number of protons increases, so that nuclei become less tightly bound as Z increases.

Electrostatic repulsion between protons plays a role in other features of the energy valley. Consider the 'parabolic' down-and-up shape of the energy for a series of nuclei with the same total number of protons and neutrons. An example is shown for 137 nucleons in the **The Energy Parabola** (previous page). For a heavy nucleus, the minimum energy (most stable nucleus) occurs when there is a particular, considerable, excess of neutrons over protons. In quantum mechanics, if the protons did not repel each other then the minimum energy would occur for equal numbers of protons and neutrons. This energy would rapidly increase when there is an unequal number of protons and neutrons. The effect of the electrostatic repulsion between the protons is dramatic: it increases the minimum energy for all nuclei, but far more for nuclei with a large excess of protons. Thus the minimum energy occurs for nuclei with more neutrons than protons, as suggested in **Displacing the Valley Bottom**. These effects become larger for heavier nuclei, which have more mutually repelling protons.

The nature of the nuclear force and the quantum rules explains the overall shape of the energy valley: the way it arcs away from the diagonal $N=Z$ line towards the neutron rich side, and the slow rise of the valley floor up towards the heavy nuclei.

Neighbours attract

Nucleons deep within a nucleus 'feel' the attractive force of nucleons surrounding them, as if they have bonds tying them to other nuclei. Nucleons at the surface have fewer such bonds, and the net result is that the total number of bonds per nucleon is much less for nuclei with fewer nucleons, since most nucleons in such nuclei are at the surface.

More about nucleon orbits

The picture of the nucleus as a droplet of nuclear matter is incomplete. Such a picture cannot explain the gullies crossing the valley at the magic numbers. To understand these we require the completely different picture of a nucleus as a collection of nucleons in orbit.

A very familiar collection of bodies in orbit is the Solar System with planets orbiting the Sun. A nucleus is very different. Firstly, there is no heavy central object like the Sun holding the nucleons in orbit. The force each nucleon feels is an average force due to all the other nucleons. Secondly, of course, protons and neutrons exist in the tiny world where quantum rules are supreme. According to these rules, it is not possible to say that a proton or neutron is 'at' some particular place, something certainly possible with planets. All that can be said is how likely it would be to find a nucleon at a particular place at a particular moment. The nuclear equivalent to the planetary orbit is the quantum orbit described by a wave function specifying the places where a nucleon would be found if its position were measured.

The fact that no more than two protons or neutrons can occupy each orbit is crucial. The idea of orbits being 'occupied' is a key to the magic numbers. In the same way that electron orbits in a hydrogen atom only have particular energies, each proton orbit corresponds to a possible energy for a proton within the nucleus. The same is true for neutrons. This means there are families, 'shells', of nucleon orbits with similar energies. Each shell has a number of available orbits, the number being determined by quantum rules. When all the orbits of a shell are occupied, we have a closed shell. For example, the isotope of tin ^{132}Sn, with 50 protons and 82 neutrons, has closed shells of both protons and neutrons, with 32 neutrons in the last, closed, neutron shell.

Thus, as protons are added to a nucleus, the orbits are filled shell by shell. When all the orbits in a shell are occupied, the nucleus is especially stable and has a lower energy than it would have otherwise. The corresponding number of protons is a magic number, and the energy of nuclei with this number of protons will dip down below the average energy of nearby nuclei – such nuclei lie in a gully crossing the energy valley. For example, since 28 and 50 are consecutive magic numbers, the shell that starts with the 29th proton, and is filled with the 50th proton, must have $50 - 28 = 22$ members. That is, it is a family of orbits that can accommodate 22 protons.

Neutron magic numbers arise in exactly the same way. The only difference is that for heavier nuclei the neutron orbits fill more easily since they do not have to worry about electrostatic repulsion. For example, the especially stable lead isotope ^{208}Pb has magic number 82 protons and magic number 126 neutrons. Something very similar occurs with atoms. These are also particularly stable when all the places in a family of electron orbits are filled. These are the atoms of the inert or 'noble' gases, such as neon and argon, see box **Periodic table of the elements**.

Periodic table of the elements

The chemical properties of the elements have a periodic behaviour. For example, the elements on the far right of the periodic table shown above – helium (He), neon (Ne), argon (Ar), krypton (Kr), xenon (Xe) and radon (Rn) – are all inert gases. They are particularly stable and do not need to form compounds with other elements. This is because their atoms have filled shells of electrons.

Period																		
1	1 H																	2 He
2	3 Li	4 Be											5 B	6 C	7 N	8 O	9 F	10 Ne
3	11 Na	12 Mg											13 Al	14 Si	15 P	16 S	17 Cl	18 Ar
4	19 K	20 Ca	21 Sc	22 Ti	23 V	24 Cr	25 Mn	26 Fe	27 Co	28 Ni	29 Cu	30 Zn	31 Ga	32 Ge	33 As	34 Se	35 Br	36 Kr
5	37 Rb	38 Sr	39 Y	40 Zr	41 Nb	42 Mo	43 Tc	44 Ru	45 Rh	46 Pd	47 Ag	48 Cd	49 In	50 Sn	51 Sb	52 Te	53 I	54 Xe
6	55 Cs	56 Ba	71 Lu	72 Hf	73 Ta	74 W	75 Re	76 Os	77 Ir	78 Pt	79 Au	80 Hg	81 Ti	82 Pb	83 Bi	84 Po	85 At	86 Rn
7	87 Fr	88 Ra	103 Lr	104 Rf	105 Db	106 Sg	107 Bh	108 Hs	109 Mt	110 Ds	111 Rg	112 Cn	113	114	115	116	117	118

57 La	58 Ce	59 Pr	60 Nd	61 Pm	62 Sm	63 Eu	64 Gd	65 Tb	66 Dy	67 Ho	68 Er	69 Tm	70 Yb
89 Ac	90 Th	91 Pa	92 U	93 Np	94 Pu	95 Am	96 Cm	97 Bk	98 Cf	99 Es	100 Fm	101 Md	102 No

1	2	3	4	5	6	7	8	9	10	11	12	13	14	15	16	17	18

Group

It seems that magic numbers begin to break down for nuclei far from the floor of the valley of stability. New accelerators and techniques make it possible to to study very short-lived nuclei with large excesses of neutrons. For example, magic number 20 is replaced by 16 and ^{24}O, with 8 protons and 16 neutrons, behaves like a doubly closed shell.

Nuclear shapes revisited

Liquid drops have a strong tendency to be spherical. This can be seen in film clips showing droplets floating in the gravity-free environment of an orbiting space station. For water droplets, as well as for nuclei, a particle in the surface feels the attractive force of fewer other particles than would be felt by a particle in the interior. So it is 'energetically favourable' to minimize the surface area, and spheres have the least possible surface area for a given volume. According to this argument, nuclei should also be spherical.

Many nuclei, however, are not spherical. This is a result of the nucleon orbits. The magic numbers mentioned above, 2, 8, 20, 28, 50, 82 and 126 apply to spherical nuclei. It turns out that there are other numbers that are 'semi-magic' if the nucleus has a non-spherical shape (referred to as deformed). This occurs because, for particular neutron numbers, the orbits for the last few neutrons are naturally deformed. For example, the isotope of the element of samarium with 86 neutrons, ^{148}Sm, is a typical spherical nucleus, but the isotope with 90 neutrons, ^{152}Sm, is prolate, that is, deformed like a rugby ball or an American football.

The energy of these orbits is lowered when the nucleus as a whole becomes deformed. As a result, nuclei with particular combinations of neutron number (or proton number) and prolate shape have lower energy than they would have otherwise. Such nuclei prefer not to be spherical. The effect of these semi-magic numbers on the energy valley is not as dramatic as the effect of the spherical magic numbers, but it is sufficient for many nuclei to be at their most stable when deformed.

For spherical nuclei, the magic numbers are well defined, so 30, 52 or 80 are definitely not magic although 28, 50 and 82 are. The number 90 marks the beginning of a whole range of neutron numbers for which the stable nuclei are deformed. This also happens with proton number 90 (thorium) so that thorium, uranium (Z=92) and plutonium (Z=94), the nuclei particularly associated with nuclear fission, are all deformed. This deformation, even for their most stable isotopes, gives these nuclei a start on the road to fission.

A deformed nucleus can be made to rotate, and this makes the phenomenon of super-deformation, described in Chapter 4, possible. When a nucleus rotates very fast, the resulting centrifugal force felt by its nucleons lowers the energy of particular highly non-spherical orbits. This results in the nucleus becoming stretched in a super-deformed shape.

Nuclear fission revisited

Today, the two pictures of nuclei – as droplets of nuclear matter, and as nucleons in orbit – are seen as complementary aspects of a more comprehensive picture. Both models provide useful insights in particular situations: they both play a role in the description of nuclear fission.

The outermost proton and neutron orbits of a uranium nucleus have a lower energy when the nucleus is deformed. The energy would be higher if the nucleus were either spherical or more deformed. The energy for such different shapes can be calculated.

The energy is lowest when the nucleus has the slight prolate deformation that uranium nuclei are found to have. To stretch a uranium nucleus until it is more deformed than its natural shape requires a great deal of energy. This can be thought of as an energy 'hill'. Once over the hill, the energy in the nucleus falls rapidly. Thus if the nucleus could become deformed just enough to get to the top of the energy hill, it would then split apart into two fragments.

The nucleons in each fragment would no longer feel the attraction from the nucleons in the other fragment, but they would still feel the effect of the electric charge of the other fragment's protons. The two fragments would thus be thrust apart with great force. The fact that there is less energy within the two fragment nuclei than the original nucleus means that a great deal of energy has been released. This becomes the energy of motion of the two fragments which interact violently with their neighbours. In this way, internal energy of the nucleus ends up as random motion of the surrounding atoms (or heat).

The only problem with this picture of nuclear fission is that the nucleus does not have enough energy to reach the top of the energy hill. Quantum mechanics provides a way for this to happen by permitting a small probability of the nucleus tunnelling through the energy hill leading to spontaneous fission. This is the same tunnelling process by which an alpha particle emerges from a nucleus in alpha decay, as Gamow showed. Sometimes energy from outside the nucleus makes it easier to surmount the fission barrier. This is what happens when a ^{235}U nucleus absorbs a neutron. The incoming neutron places the resulting 'compound nucleus' ^{236}U in an excited state and the extra energy allows it to overcome the fission barrier.

Neutron stars: the largest nuclei

One force of Nature has been ignored completely in our account of nuclei, the force of gravity. It is 10^{40} times weaker than the electrostatic force and makes absolutely no measurable contribution to the binding of atomic nuclei. It is certainly important to us, however, being the reason we do not require tethering to Earth with ropes.

Gravity differs from the electromagnetic force in that there are no such things as 'like' and 'unlike' gravitational charges: everything attracts everything else and there is no repulsion. In spite of the electromagnetic force being immensely more powerful than gravity, almost everything around us on the macroscopic scale is neutral and electric forces mostly go unnoticed. When natural processes do separate just a little positive and negative charge, they tend to get back together quite dramatically. An example of this is lightning.

In spite of the weakness of gravity, there do exist 'nuclear' systems in the cosmos where gravity plays a crucial role. These are neutron stars. When a giant star, many times the mass of the Sun, comes to the end of its life, it undergoes a colossal explosion, becoming a supernova and briefly shines as brightly as an entire galaxy. If the conditions are right, it leaves behind a compact object about 10 to 15 km across (the size of a city) but with a mass at least 1.4 times that of the Sun. It consists largely of neutrons, the protons in the core of the star having combined with electrons under the pressure of the explosion to form neutrons and neutrinos. The neutrons remain as a neutron star. Vast quantities of neutrinos spread through space at the speed of light. In spite of their weak interactions with matter, a few might be detected on Earth in underground detectors like Kamiokande in Japan, see **Supernova neutrinos**.

Surprisingly, perhaps, many of the properties of neutron stars can be understood directly from the properties of the 'nuclear matter' within nuclei. This is a huge extrapolation since the largest atomic nuclei have about 300 nucleons. Gravity acting within neutron stars makes it possible to have a bound object with about 10^{53} times as many nucleons, most of which are neutrons. It is remarkable that information from the shape of the energy valley can be extended all the way to neutron stars.

A crucial property is the fact that nuclear matter is hard to compress. The pressure due to gravity acting at the centre of an object 10 km across, but with a mass greater than the Sun, is enormous. In spite of this pressure, the average density of a neutron star is somewhat more than that of an atomic nucleus: about 3×10^{14} times as dense as water. Only at the very centre does the pressure make it perhaps three or four times as dense as ordinary nuclei. In October 2010, a neutron star with twice that mass of the Sun was announced. This is the most massive neutron star yet discovered, and may well be near the limit, since greater mass will lead to the formation of a black hole.

Neutron stars are sometimes close companions of 'normal' stars in a binary star system; many stars are really binaries in which two stars rotate about their common centre of mass. Sometimes material from the normal star lands on the surface of the neutron star with spectacular results, as shown in **Explosion on a neutron star**. The enormous energy released includes copious X-rays. Many of the sources discovered by X-ray telescopes are of this kind.

Supernova neutrinos

A pulse of neutrinos from supernova SN 1987A arrived on cue at the Kamiokande observatories underground neutrino detector in Japan. The designation 1987A identifies the supernova as the first to be observed in 1987. The expected neutron star left over after this supernova explosion has not been seen, either because it is hidden by dust, or because a black hole was created instead.

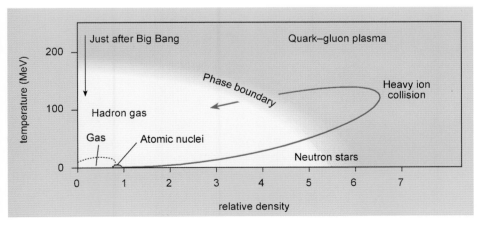

Hot, dense nuclear stuff

All nuclei have much the the same density, and unless they have been heated up in a nuclear collision they are 'cold'. But nuclear material can be compressed to a higher degree in neutron stars and heated up in supernova explosions. The Big Bang was exceptionally hot, and nuclear material then took the form of quark–gluon plasma, which is a different phase of nuclear material; much as ice and steam are different phases of water. In a collision between heavy nuclei at very high energies, nuclear matter will follow the path of the green line. This takes it out into the quark–gluon plasma region.

While the general properties of neutron stars are reasonably well understood, they raise many interesting questions that have yet to be answered. The full understanding of neutron stars demands a more detailed knowledge of the behaviour of nuclear matter at high temperatures and pressures. This is a powerful motivation for many experiments at accelerator laboratories such as RHIC in the USA and now at the LHC at CERN in which high energy heavy nuclei are smashed together, producing for a brief instant some of the conditions within both neutron stars and the explosions which gave birth to them.

Explosion on a neutron star

This series of images is a computer artist's concept of a rare explosion on a neutron star, which is the dead core of a massive star. The neutron star's strong gravity pulls gas from a nearby companion star (blue sphere in Image 1). The gas forms a disk as it flows on to the neutron star, like water pouring down a drain (red area in Image 2). Since a neutron star has about the mass of the Sun compressed into a sphere only about 10 miles (16 km) across, it is incredibly dense. This gives the star tremendous gravity, about 300,000 times greater than Earth's surface gravity, which compresses the gas as it builds up on the surface of the neutron star. Eventually, pressure and heat in the gas on the surface becomes so high that the gas detonates in a tremendous nuclear fusion explosion. The explosion distorts and illuminates the gas disk (Images 3 and 4). A detailed rendering of the neutron star surface before the explosion is shown in Image 5, and Image 6 reveals what the surface might look like during the explosion. The actual orbital motion of the two stars is quite complex and has been simplified to focus on the details of the explosion. (NASA/Dana Berry)

3.

4.

5.

6.

The discovery of neutron stars – Jocelyn Bell Burnell

Jocelyn Bell Burnell and the Cambridge radio telescope. (Courtesy Jocelyn Bell Burnell.)

In the late 1960s quasars (quasi-stellar radio sources) had recently been discovered to be very distant, luminous objects which allowed the study of an early phase of the Universe. A radio survey of the sky, to discover more of them was started in Cambridge (UK). The radio telescope specially built, in-house, for the project spread over 2 hectares and consisted of 2,048 dipoles operating at 81.5 MHz. The signals received by the radio telescope were recorded on strips of paper chart (no computers were available). The sky was repeatedly surveyed, each scan lasting 4 days, and producing 120 metres of paper chart. As the research student on the project I was responsible for running the survey and analysing the paper charts.

Occasionally on those 120 metres of chart there was about 0.5 centimetres of signal that puzzled me. It did not look like a quasar, nor did it did it look like locally generated radio interference that intermittently swamped the weak cosmic radio signals. The curious signal was very weak, was often not present, and moved across the sky with the stars.

Just as I focussed attention on it, it weakened and dropped to a level where we could not detect it. For a month I made special but fruitless visits to the observatory. Then it reappeared, and I could see that the signal was a string of pulses, equally spaced at about 1.3 seconds. The next month was one of worry; this signal was so unexpected we suspected something was wrong. However, it was not a fault with the radio telescope or receiver, for a colleague's telescope could pick it up too. Was it a satellite in an unusual orbit, or radar signals bouncing off the Moon and into the telescope? No. The pulse repetition rate was fast, implying a small object, but the pulse rate was very accurately maintained, implying a big object with large reservoirs of energy. Then we got an estimate of the distance to the source, which placed it far beyond the Solar System, but well within our Galaxy.

Then I discovered a second such source. It was in a different direction in space, and pulsed at a slightly different rate, but appeared to be of the same family of objects. It was immediately clear that we had stumbled over an unsuspected type of star. A few weeks later I discovered a third and a fourth.

Over the next six months we realized that these pulsars (pulsating radio stars) were neutron stars, sweeping a radio beam around the sky each time they rotated. Neutron stars were both small (in diameter) and big (in mass). Now over 1000 are known.

9. Cosmic furnaces

The stars and the birth of elements

Life on Earth depends entirely upon the Sun. So vital is its light and warmth that, from ancient times, it has often been worshipped. More recently, we have come to understand that not only do we rely on our local star to sustain us, but that we actually exist because of other, long dead, stars. The Earth, and almost everything on it, is made from the ashes of giant stars that lived their lives and then exploded billions of years ago. The Solar System itself, to which the Sun, planets and humans belong, came into being around 4.5 billion years ago, condensing out of the gas and dust ejected by an earlier generation of stars in their death throes. There is an abundance of carbon, oxygen and iron, all vital to life, because carbon, oxygen and iron nuclei were produced and expelled as those early stars died.

How stars shine and how the elements were produced, are two stories linked by nuclear physics experiments. Nuclear processes in stars can be understood by studying them on Earth; we can even attempt to tap the same source of energy that powers the Sun.

Apart from the fact that we depend on the Sun, the points made above are far from obvious. For example, in the 1830s the philosopher Auguste Comte claimed that the composition of the stars was an example of something that would always be beyond human knowledge. This statement was quite acceptable before the birth of spectroscopy.

More than two millennia before Comte, Aristotle made a proclamation which soon became dogma: "Everything in the heavens," he said, "is made of perfect, unchanging and incorruptible 'quintessence'." One reason Galileo Galilei was unpopular with the authorities was that some of his discoveries challenged this view. The idea that experiments on Earth might mimic processes in stars contradicted what people had believed for two thousand years. Such experiments are now carried out; stars are not made of 'quintessence' – essentially, they are composed of the same basic material as us.

A great physicist of the Victorian era, Lord Kelvin, proclaimed that the Sun could not be more than 100 million years old – a correct deduction based on the sources of energy known at that time. Geologists and biologists had strong reasons to believe that the Earth was much older, and in 1903 Rutherford pointed out the apparently continuous energy flowing out of radioactive nuclei showed "the maintenance of solar energy no longer presented a fundamental problem."

The nuclear physics pioneer, **George Gamow**, proposed that all the elements were produced in the Big Bang. This was a sensible deduction based on scientific knowledge of the 1940s, but Nature is an inexhaustible source of surprises and one of these was the discovery of technetium in certain red giant stars. This short-lived element could not have been made in the Big Bang 13.7 billion years ago, so that

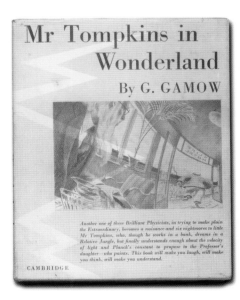

George Gamow, popular science writer

George Gamow showed how alpha particles tunnel out of nuclei with the help of quantum theory. The same theory shows how pairs of nuclei could tunnel inwards and fuse together. This opens the door to understanding how energy is produced in stars and how heavy elements are made from lighter elements, ultimately from hydrogen. Gamow was also the father of Big Bang cosmology and the author of a much-loved series of popular physics books, still in print. (Courtesy Cambridge University Press.)

some elements, at least, must be produced in stars. This is now firmly establishe[d]

We now understand that the hydrogen and helium from the Big Bang have undergone fusion in successive generations of stars, producing new element[s] along the way. Stars and planetary systems, like ours, are formed from the d[ust] and gases from stars whose lives have ended explosively. We can see this ha[p]pening: in **The Orion Nebula** bright regions can be seen where new stars a[re] being born from the ashes of dead stars. As the material swirls together und[er] gravity, it will heat and ignite to form new stars and planetary systems. This [is] how our solar system was formed, enriched by elements that had been made in stars, now dead.

The abundance of the elements

Gamow's idea that the elements were made in the Big Bang was not entire[ly] wrong. At present, the observable matter in the Universe is roughly 70% hydrogen, 28% helium and only about 2% everything else. (These percenta[ges] are by mass, not by number of atoms.) The hydrogen and most of the heliu[m], together with some lithium (element 3) were produced in the Big Bang, but every other element has been produced in stars. The 2% that Gamow was wrong about includes the carbon, oxygen, nitrogen, iron and all the other elements.

We referred to the *observable* matter in the Universe out of respect for the f[act] that it is now clear that the Universe contains a large fraction of dark matt[er], matter that does not light up in stars. The nature of dark matter is the subj[ect] of intense discussion and experiment. Only one thing is agreed on: it is not composed of 'baryonic' matter, i.e. protons, neutrons and other particles ma[de] of quarks and gluons. It also seems to interact very weakly with ordinary ma[t]ter, and is probably passing through us all the time, making experiments to detect it extremely difficult. From this point on, this chapter is concerned w[ith] only ordinary non-dark matter, although dark matter is of great importance [to] the Universe as a whole through its gravitational effects.

It is not a trivial job to determine the cosmic abundances of the elements, that is, what proportion of each element, or what proportion of each kind o[f] atomic nucleus exists in the Universe. Many places are untypical in that the[y] will contain a higher concentration of certain species than elsewhere – for example a jeweller's shop would not be a suitable place to estimate the cos[mic] abundance of gold.

The spectrum of the light from stars is one important source of information about the cosmic abundance of elements. In Chapter 2, see **Atomic fingerprints**, we showed black absorption lines in stellar spectra. These are forme[d] as the light passes through the cooler outer layers of the star, as suggested i[n] **Shining through a star's atmosphere**.

Meteorites found on Earth also carry information about the abundances of [dif]ferent elements, see **Messenger from Space**. Certain kinds of meteorites ar[e] known to date back to the formation of the Solar System, and these reveal [a] consistent pattern of element proportions (the Solar System abundances) a[nd] these are in fair agreement with that found in typical stars. The compositio[n] of each star depends upon the star's history, but an overall pattern emerges.

The Orion Nebula

This famous nebula is found just below the belt in the constellation of Orion. The belt of Orion can be seen as the three stars across the middle of the upper image, by Pete Lawrence. The nebula appears as a hazy patch in binoculars, or even with the naked eye from dark locations. Within it is a region of a thousand young stars crowded into a space less than the distance from our Sun to its nearest neighbouring stars. This is a stellar nursery where a new generation of stars is being born. The false colour image, lower, taken in the infrared region of the electromagnetic spectrum, allows us to look deep into the region. (Courtesy European Southern Observatories.)

Long wavelength

Short wavelength

There are vast differences in the proportions of each element. For example, in the Earth's crust there is a million times greater abundance of oxygen than of platinum. Clearly there is some influence from the energy valley, with elements located beyond iron and nickel being much less abundant than the lighter elements. Elements with magic numbers of protons tend to be more common, see **Cosmic Abundances**.

By and large, the lightest elements are the most common. Somehow, the elements must come from a series of nuclear processes that start with hydrogen and build progressively heavier nuclei. There is a lot of carbon and oxygen because, in many stars, the sequence of nucleus building can only reach as far as these elements.

From hydrogen to helium

Almost all the energy we receive from the Sun comes from a series of reactions in which protons (hydrogen nuclei) interact to make helium nuclei. These reactions are also the first step towards the production of all the other elements. The process begins when two protons are attracted to each other and make a new nucleus, but there are two factors which work against this happening. The first is that although

10 mm

Messenger from space

The light-coloured 'chondrules' visible in this meteorite, Adrar 303, have elements in the same proportion as the gas and dust from which the Solar System condensed. The proportion of different nuclei is remarkably close to what is found in many stars, representing the cosmic nuclear abundance. (Courtesy Ian Franchi, The Open University.)

the nuclear force is strong and attractive when the protons are close, it is actually very hard for the protons to get near enough to each other for the force to be felt. This is because of the other force between protons, the electrostatic repulsion, keeping the two like-charged protons apart. The second problem is that the nuclear force is not quite strong enough to bind two protons; a nucleus consisting of two protons, ^{2}He, does not exist.

Neither of these problems exist if we begin with binding a proton and a neutron together. Since the neutron carries no electrical charge, there is no electrostatic repulsion acting against this pairing, and protons and neutrons do form a 'bound state': the deuteron (the nucleus of the isotope of hydrogen ^{2}H). While this would have happened during the Big Bang when there were free neutrons around, all the neutrons that did not pair up with protons will have undergone beta decay long ago. Free neutrons cannot survive longer than a few minutes before turning into protons. With none of these free neutrons remaining today, we are restricted to the fusion of two protons.

The consequences of this electrostatic repulsion between two protons can be overcome in stars by a combination of quantum mechanics and high temperatures. The same rule of quantum mechanics that allows alpha particles to tunnel out of certain nuclei, enables protons with sufficient energy to tunnel through the force barrier between them. Protons at room temperature would certainly not have sufficient energy, but the temperature at the centre of the Sun is about 15 million degrees Kelvin. Consequently, a tiny fraction of the protons do have enough energy to penetrate the electrostatic barrier.

Having tunnelled through the barrier, the protons must still face the problem that there is no bound state of two protons. This problem is overcome by one of the protons turning into a neutron via beta decay, emitting a positron and a neutrino.

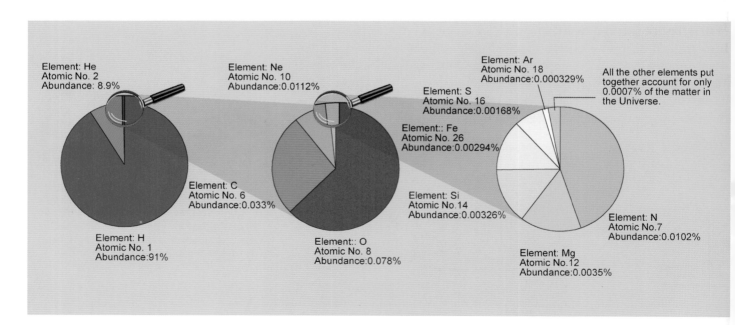

Cosmic abundances

In this pie chart the percentages indicate the relative number of atoms, so the percentage of the lightest atoms, such as those of hydrogen, is greater than the percentages when they are expressed by weight.

This complete process requires three of the four forces of Nature acting in coordination against the fourth. The gravitational force first compresses the hydrogen gas, raising its temperature and giving the protons the necessary energy to tunnel together. Next, the strong nuclear force keeps them close together while the weak nuclear force causes one of them to turn into a neutron, allowing the formation of the deuteron. During the process, the electromagnetic force acts to keep the two protons apart.

On average, it takes billions of years for protons in the Sun to join up to become deuterons because the transformation of a proton into a neutron happens very slowly. Once the deuteron is formed, the next step is much more rapid. Within seconds of being produced, a deuteron and another proton will tunnel together through the barrier between them to form the isotope of helium, ^{3}He. This is shown in the first two steps of **From hydrogen to helium**.

The ^{3}He nuclei survive somewhat longer than the deuterons, but they too will quickly disappear. Being positively charged, two ^{3}He nuclei will repel one another, but if they have enough energy they have a chance of fusing. If they do this, not all six nucleons will stick together, but a ^{4}He nucleus (alpha particle) will be formed and the two redundant protons will be emitted. The overall effect of this series of reactions is for six protons to form an alpha particle, with two protons left over, a process known as the 'pp chain'. The fusion of hydrogen to helium also produces the energy that keeps the Sun in its present steady state, lasting billions of years. The energy released as hydrogen undergoes fusion in the fifteen million degree heat of the Sun's core, steadily travels to the much cooler surface, where it is radiated into space. The outflowing energy also powers violent processes that render the Sun's tenuous atmosphere much hotter than the surface so that some of the fusion energy is ultimately transmitted as ultra violet radiation, see **The ultraviolet Sun**.

The first step, the fusion of two protons, is the bottleneck of the pp chain. It takes place too slowly for it ever to be observed on Earth, but the reaction between two ^{3}He nuclei can be measured. These very difficult measurements, first made at **LUNA** (Laboratory for Underground Nuclear Astrophysics, see **LUNA**) in a

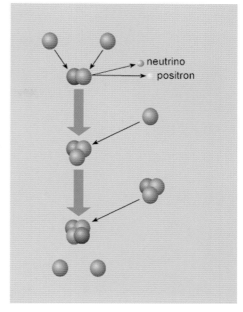

From hydrogen to helium

These are the reactions taking place at the core of the Sun. When two protons (red) collide they occasionally tunnel together. One proton becomes a neutron (blue) releasing a neutrino and a positron. The deuteron formed in this reaction rapidly absorbs another proton yielding a ^{3}He nucleus which reacts with another forming a ^{4}He nucleus and two protons. This chain of events in which four protons become a helium nucleus is the main source of energy in the Sun. This energy is eventually radiated from the surface of the Sun.

LUNA

Luna is the Laboratory for Underground Nuclear Astrophysics located at the Laboratori Nazionali del Gran Sasso in Italy. The picture shows the array of underground laboratories, all carrying out research that requires the shielding from cosmic rays by many metres of rock. (Courtesy LUNA.)

The ultraviolet Sun

This image shows the ultraviolet radiation emitted by the Sun's tenuous upper atmosphere at a temperature of one million degrees. (Courtesy SOHO, a project of ESA and NASA.)

tunnel deep beneath the Gran Sasso Mountains in Italy, help provide a firm basis for the detailed models of the internal workings of the Sun and other stars which are such a major part of modern astrophysics.

For most of its life, the Sun is, in effect, a factory for turning hydrogen into helium. Eventually, this process must end as the hydrogen at the centre of the Sun, where it is hot enough for fusion to take place, becomes exhausted. The core starts to contract and becomes even hotter, reaching the region of 100 million degrees. This is hot enough for the common isotope of carbon, ^{12}C, to be produced via the 'triple-alpha process'. While this is happening, the Sun's surface expands and the Sun becomes a red giant, eventually ejecting some of its outer layers into space. Some of this material will find its way into the next generation of stars and possible planetary systems.

The triple-alpha process – a very delicate balance

Like all carbon-based creatures, we humans depend on the production of carbon in stars. The natural way for ^{12}C to be produced would be for two ^4He nuclei to tunnel through the repulsive barrier between them to form a nucleus of the beryllium isotope ^8Be. Another ^4He nucleus would then tunnel in to make a nucleus of ^{12}C. Unfortunately, the ^8Be nucleus is not quite bound, and almost as soon as it forms it splits back into two alphas. It has the unimaginably small lifetime of about 10^{-16} seconds giving very little opportunity for another alpha particle to join up with it to form carbon.

The situation is saved by a 'resonance'. A resonance allows a radio to be tuned so that it is millions of times more sensitive to radio waves of a certain frequency than signals of all other frequencies. Similarly, nuclei have certain energies at which they are very much more likely to be formed in a reaction. ^{12}C has a resonance at exactly the right energy to allow alpha particles to exploit the extremely short-lived ^8Be nuclei in stars for carbon to be produced. Without this resonance at just the right energy, carbon-based life would not exist. It has been estimated that if the strength of the nuclear force were to be changed by one part in 200, then the production of ^{12}C nuclei would be thirty times less. The Universe is extraordinarily finely tuned!

The vital resonance in ^{12}C is often called the Hoyle resonance after the astronomer **Fred Hoyle** who predicted its existence, around 1950, on the grounds that it just had to exist in order for many elements to be produced. In 1953, the Hoyle resonance was shown to exist in experiments at Caltech in California. In these experiments, deuterons were fired from an accelerator at a target containing the nitrogen isotope ^{14}N, producing alpha particles, ^4He, and ^{12}C in the resonant state.

Elements and energy in more massive stars

The Sun, along with other stars of the same mass or less, will never produce substantial amounts of nuclei heavier than ^{12}C, but such nuclei must have existed in the cloud from which the Solar System condensed … so where did the heavy elements come from?

The Sun is a star of about average mass, but some stars are 10 or even a hundred times more massive. Theory suggests that 120 to 150 solar masses is the upper limit, but there do seem to be a few stars that defy that limit. It is the

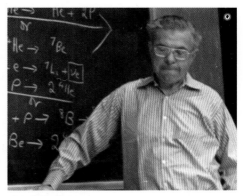

Fred Hoyle

Fred Hoyle, 1915-2001, made many contributions to astronomy and cosmology, particularly his theories of how elements are formed in the stars. (AIP Emilio Segré Archive.)

more massive stars that produce the heavier elements. The more massive the star, the hotter it is and the more rapidly it passes through all the stages of its existence. The heaviest stars have quite short lifetimes and often end their lives in catastrophic supernova explosions, ejecting much of their matter into space for recycling. Apart from hydrogen, almost all the atoms in our bodies and the world around us have been ejected from stars. Most of the heaviest elements, such as gold and uranium, were created in supernova explosions.

A high temperature is the key to making heavy elements. All nuclei, being positively charged, repel each other. The greater the charges, the stronger this repulsion between them. The rate at which quantum mechanics allows them to **tunnel** through the repulsive energy barrier depends very sensitively on how much energy they have due to their motion (kinetic energy) compared to the height of the barrier. A higher barrier means the nuclei need more energy to get through at a given rate, and this is where temperature is so important. The energy of a nucleus within a star increases with the temperature at its location. The hottest part of a star is its core, at the centre. Since heat travels from hotter to cooler regions, the energy flows out from the core to the cooler outer regions of the star from where it is radiated into space.

At present, the centre of the Sun is hot enough for hydrogen to fuse to make helium, but not hot enough for the triple-alpha process, and certainly not hot enough for the fusion of heavier nuclei. The temperature of the core will rise dramatically when it collapses after its hydrogen runs out. The triple-alpha fusion reaction ignites at about 100 million degrees. For stars more massive than the Sun, changes of this kind increase the core temperature even more, allowing much heavier nuclei to form.

Using carbon to make helium

In stars more massive than the Sun, there is an alternative to the pp chain method of producing helium from hydrogen. This is the CNO (carbon–nitrogen–oxygen) cycle, first proposed by Nobel prize winner **Hans Bethe** in the late 1930s. This process requires a star to have at least a trace of ^{12}C mixed in with the hydrogen. In this event, a ^{12}C nucleus can absorb a proton to produce a nucleus of the nitrogen isotope ^{13}N, see the box **CNO Cycle**. Within a few minutes, the ^{13}N nucleus undergoes beta decay, turning into the carbon isotope ^{13}C, which is stable. Another proton will then tunnel through the ^{13}C barrier to produce ^{14}N. This nucleus is also stable and will eventually absorb another proton to become ^{15}O, a radioactive nucleus lasting just a couple of minutes before beta decaying to ^{15}N. The cycle finishes when ^{15}N absorbs a proton and an alpha particle is emitted leaving a ^{12}C nucleus, the starting point of the cycle.

The net effect of the CNO cycle is the same as the pp chain. Four protons, ordinary hydrogen nuclei, combine to produce a ^{4}He nucleus plus two positrons, two neutrinos and energy. In the CNO cycle, ^{12}C acts as a catalyst: it enables the process to take place, but is still there at the end. The CNO cycle certainly powers many of the stars shining today, but it would but would not have taken place in the very earliest stars that condensed out of the material produced in the Big Bang as that matter contained no carbon.

Using up the hydrogen

Towards the end of their lives, as the hydrogen in their cores becomes depleted, stars expand and become red giants. The Sun will enter its red giant phase in about

Tunnel: Tunnelling *inwards* here depends on energy in exactly the same way as tunnelling *outwards* in alpha decay. We have seen earlier how Gamow applied the quantum theory of tunnelling to explain how the half-lives of alpha-decaying nuclei depend so sensitively on the energy of the emitted alpha particle.

Hans Bethe

Hans Bethe (1905-2005) was awarded the Nobel Prize in physics in 1967 particularly for his discovery of the processes for energy production in stars. Bethe made major contributions to a wide range of physics over 7 decades of active research. He is seen here giving a lecture in Paris in 1956. (AIP Emilio Segré Visual Archives.)

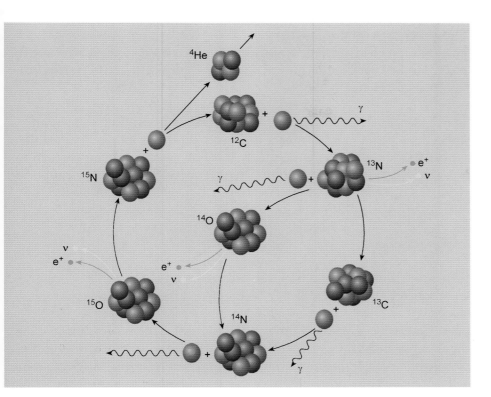

CNO cycle

The CNO cycle takes place in hot stars. Four protons become an alpha particle (^{4}He nucleus) plus two electrons and two anti-neutrinos, indicated by the Greek letter nu (ν). Energy is released, partly as gamma rays (γ). The CNO cycle requires the presence of carbon nuclei ^{12}C, and the cycle starts when these absorb protons.

five billion years and its outer atmosphere will extend to completely envelop the inner planets. Stars that are more massive than the Sun go through their red giant phase sooner, achieving particularly high temperatures deep within them as they do so. This enables a range of element-producing reactions to occur. Material ejected from the outer layers of red giant stars is believed to be the main source of the carbon and nitrogen upon which life depends.

Once ^{4}He and ^{12}C nuclei are created, a common process occurs by which they fuse to make ^{16}O; this requires a temperature of about 500 million degrees. At higher temperatures still, tunnelling between nuclei becomes easier and so a great many different reactions take place. For example, pairs of ^{12}C nuclei or ^{16}O nuclei can fuse together. Although there are many other reactions taking place, including those involving the absorption of protons, it is the occurrence of these processes which partly explains why, as we saw in Chapter 5, nuclei which are multiples of the alpha particle, such as the common isotopes of carbon and oxygen, are abundant on Earth. Another reason for this abundance is that these nuclei are particularly stable, making them less likely to be decomposed by gamma rays. At temperatures around a billion degrees, there exists a huge flux of gamma ray photons that can break up nuclei, especially the less stable ones.

At the centre of stars much heavier than the Sun, there eventually comes a rather brief period when temperatures reach around 4 billion degrees. At this temperature ^{4}He can fuse with the isotope of silicon, ^{28}Si, and heavier nuclei.

Nuclei of elements all the way up to iron are thus both created and destroyed, until there is a state of equilibrium in which the most stable isotopes mostly predominate. Some of these will be ejected into space. The shape of the energy valley means that very few of the elements lying much past iron and nickel are made in this process. It is not a coincidence that the Earth's core is believed to be largely composed of iron and nickel.

The lead in your car battery

There is no problem with producing elements with up to 26 or 28 protons: iron and nickel. Beyond these, all the way up to lead (with 82 protons), ways have to be found to make them.

Some red giant stars generate large numbers of neutrons. When a neutron strikes a nucleus it may go straight through, but often it will be absorbed. If the new nucleus is stable, it will simply shake off any excess energy as gamma rays and wait for the next neutron. On other occasions, the extra neutron places the nucleus too far up the neutron-rich side of the energy valley; the nucleus now has too many neutrons, causing the nucleus to undergo beta decay. The neutron will become a proton and the Z of the nucleus will increase by one.

In these neutron-rich stars, the nucleus will continue to be bathed in neutrons and another neutron will be absorbed. The effect is that the nucleus works its way along the floor of the energy valley towards heavier and heavier nuclei. If the nucleus gets too high up the neutron-rich side, it will slide back down by emitting the electrons and anti-neutrinos of beta decay. This process, known as the 'slow process' or 's-process', produces many of the isotopes of elements heavier than iron and nickel, see **The s-process**. This process ends with the bismuth isotope ^{209}Bi.

The s-process cannot be the whole story. Not all isotopes of the heavy elements are made in the s-process. The closed shell dips, or gullies, that cross the energy valley, tend to stop the s-process happening. The gullies represent nuclei with certain numbers of neutrons that are particularly stable and have lower energies than their neighbours. Such nuclei with closed neutron shells

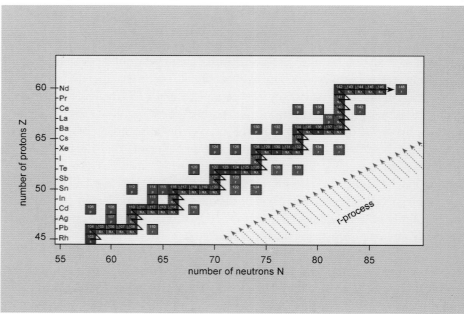

The s-process

The black line follows part of the s-process from iron to bismuth, which takes about 100 years. When a nucleus absorbs a neutron the path steps one nucleus to the right. After a series of such steps, the nucleus undergoes beta decay, stepping diagonally up and to the left and then continues to absorb neutrons. The s-process occurs in red giant stars and the elements produced are indicated by blue squares. Some elements shown are made by other processes – red squares indicate elements made in the r-process (shown later in this chapter) in supernova explosions. Squares which are both red and blue indicate elements formed in both processes. Green squares represent nuclei made by the p-process, in which protons are captured.

do not readily pick up additional neutrons, so the path to new elements is halted.

The s-process can make lead, and is a major source of iodine, essential for life. Another element made in this way is technetium, which does not exist naturally on Earth. The longest-living isotope of technetium lives just a few million years. The observation of the spectroscopic signature of technetium in stars is strong evidence that the s-process occurs within them since the half-life is so much shorter than the ages of the stars.

The s-process cannot produce about half of the stable isotopes that are heavier than iron, including gold and all the isotopes of uranium and thorium. The existence on Earth of these elements is proof that there must be another process taking place. In addition, many elements have quite a few stable isotopes a short way up the neutron-rich side of the energy valley that are generally not made by the s-process.

When a star outshines a galaxy

Uranium, thorium and many other heavy nuclei are produced in the enormous explosions which are the dying throes of stars with ten or more times the mass of the Sun. Such an explosion is a supernova. For a short while, a supernova outshines the whole galaxy, leaving behind a much less massive remnant as its outer layers are blasted off to become part of the interstellar medium. The remnant left behind is often a neutron star, but certain heavy stars might leave behind a black hole.

The element-making process associated with a supernova is known as the 'rapid' or 'r-process'. The path of the r-process is shown in **The r-process**. The core of certain (type II) supernovae release a vast flood of neutrons, far more than were present during the s-process, see **Type II supernova explosions**, and **Type II supernova – final stages**. Exposed to such an intense flux, a nucleus in the outer layers absorbs many neutrons much more rapidly than it undergoes beta decay. As a result, such a nucleus finds itself some distance up the neutron-rich side of the energy valley. Eventually, the nucleus becomes so unstable that it tumbles down the valley in a cascade of electrons and neutrinos. In this way, the r-process

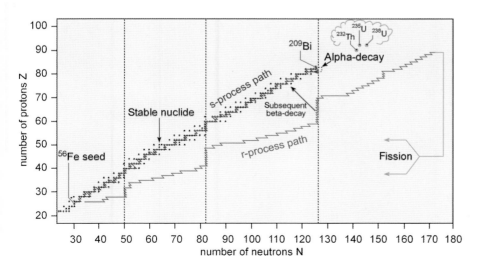

The r-process

The huge flux of neutrons from a supernova leads to the r-process in which very short-lived nuclei are produced far up the neutron-rich side of the energy valley. These subsequently beta decay down towards the floor of the valley. All the uranium and thorium on Earth was produced by the r-process.

produces some nuclei that the s-process does not, uranium being an example.

Many nuclei on the r-process paths lie so far from the valley floor that they have never been made or studied on Earth. This has spurred intense experimental activity to study nuclei out towards the neutron dripline. Detailed information about such very neutron-rich nuclei is an essential ingredient of theoretical models of the r-process. This is required for a full understanding both of supernovae and of the origin of the elements. Currently much research effort is devoted to understanding the structure and properties of the nuclei that take part in the r-process. Such nuclei have a very large neutron excess and live very briefly and so must be studied in a tiny fraction of a second of the instant when they are made. There are a few laboratories around the world where such studies are made, and **RNCP Osaka Laboratory** (see next page) shows part of one of them.

Fusion power on Earth

It has been a dream of scientists for half a century to reproduce and harness the fusion reactions that power the Sun. If successful, this process could provide a clean and inexhaustible supply of energy to help meet ever-expanding world demand.

The fusion of two hydrogen nuclei to produce helium is accompanied by the release of energy, but it is necessary to have enormous temperatures before the two hydrogen nuclei are energetic enough to fuse. Scientists face the problem of maintaining and containing such temperatures. In addition, the reaction employed cannot be that of two protons fusing together as it occurs far too slowly. Most practical schemes would have to involve the fusion of heavier isotopes of hydrogen such as deuterium and tritium. Fusion researchers use a machine called a Tokamak as a kind of test-bed for proving the principles of confined and controlled nuclear fusion on Earth, but while progress is being made, it will be many years before such an energy source is developed.

Type II supernova explosions

A supergiant star with an iron core exhausts its fuel, and when fusion ceases there is no longer any pressure to hold up the outer layers which collapse inwards. This causes huge pressure at its centre and the outer layers bounce out in a stupendous explosion releasing more energy at a stroke than the star has output in its entire life up to this point.

Supergiant

RCNP Osaka Laboratory

The Grand-Raiden spectrometer at the RNCP Osaka Laboratory in Japan studies, among other things, briefly existing r-process nuclei. A beam carrying energetic particles from a large accelerator enters through the beam tube enclosed in square-shaped magnets. These magnets keep the beam focussed. The energetic particles then collide with a target in a stainless steel chamber. Some of the products then pass through large bending magnets (somewhat like small segments of a huge circle) and other products of the reaction are measured in the large chamber to the right. (Courtesy RCNP Osaka Laboratory.)

Shock wave

Neutron star

Expanding shell
of gas

Type II supernova - final stages

The high pressures cause electrons and protons to combine to form neutrons and an immense pulse of neutrinos producing a shock wave which ejects the outer layers into space, leaving behind a neutron star. If the original star is sufficiently massive, the result will be a black hole. The flux of neutrons leads to the production of new elements which are dispersed in space.

JET, the Joint European Torus

JET is located at Culham, near Oxford in the UK. Deuterium and tritium ions, held in place by strong magnetic fields, are made to collide and fuse within the donut-shaped vacuum chamber. The cut-away shows the huge magnetic pole-pieces around the vacuum vessel. The height inside the vacuum vessel is more than 4 metres and the whole apparatus is 12 metres high. JET is just part of the long and difficult international effort to harness fusion energy for peaceful purposes on Earth. (Photographs courtesy EFDA–JET.)

The time scale for fusion is long. In 1973, design work began for the international **JET, the Joint European Torus** Tokamak. JET's first plasma was in 1983, and JET generated the world's first controlled fusion energy in 1991. In 2011, JET is still testing ideas for ITER the next step towards fusion power. In 2010, a ten year international collaboration to build ITER began in France. ITER is a large scale Tokamak with the design target of producing, from nuclear fusion, ten times more power than it consumes.

The big picture

We have now met most of the ways that nuclei are made in stars. The initial hydrogen from the Big Bang fuses within the hot cores of stars, producing helium, which adds to the helium already produced just after the Big Bang. When the hydrogen in a star has been consumed, a succession of changes begins. The details of these changes depend on the mass of the star. In the heaviest stars, quite large amounts of elements up to iron are produced. Beyond that there is a precipitous drop in production, but significant amounts of copper and zinc (elements 29 and 30) are produced. These elements are essential for life, but only a few beyond them are, such as selenium (34), molybdenum (42) and iodine (53).

For elements such as these, the stable isotopes with the largest neutron numbers tend to be made in the r-process, whereas the stable isotopes at the very bottom of the energy valley tend to be made by the s-process.

There are also other processes at work. For example, certain supernovae, known as type Ia, appear to produce huge fluxes of protons instead of neutrons, see **Type Ia supernova explosion**. These give rise to the 'rapid proton' or 'rp-process'. This is similar to the r-process except that it operates on the proton-rich side of the energy valley. A nucleus absorbs several protons before it has a chance to undergo beta decay. The rp-process produces certain proton-rich isotopes that could not otherwise be made.

Another remarkable feature of these supernovae is the production of huge amounts of the unstable isotope of nickel, ^{56}Ni. This nucleus has 28 protons and 28 neutrons and is therefore a doubly closed shell nucleus. It is presumably formed by the successive fusion of 14 alpha particles, but a nucleus as far as ^{56}Ni from the floor of the energy valley cannot be stable even if it does have closed shells of both protons and neutrons. A ^{56}Ni nucleus has a considerable excess of energy, which it releases by beta decaying first to ^{56}Co (cobalt) and then to ^{56}Fe. When the star explodes, the energy released by these beta decays heats up the ejected material, contributing to the spectacular visible displays made by these supernovae.

Yet another process is responsible for producing certain light nuclei such as the lithium isotope ^{6}Li. Although a small amount of another lithium isotope, ^{7}Li, was made in the Big Bang, ^{6}Li was not. In addition, it is not made in stars – on the contrary, stars destroy it. The isotope ^{6}Li, along with the beryllium isotope ^{9}Be, are made by a process known as spallation, which follows the collision of a very high-energy proton with a ^{12}C or ^{16}O nucleus in interstellar space. Such high energy protons are a major part of the cosmic rays that bombard the Earth from all directions. When such a high energy proton strikes the heavier nucleus, it smashes it, producing a variety of lighter nuclei, known as spallation products, including ^{6}Li and ^{9}Be, which are not made elsewhere.

It is not surprising that there is still uncertainty about the very complex processes in which heavy nuclei are made. Much of our understanding comes from painstaking measurements on unimaginably remote stars. A sample of material can never be taken directly from stars, but we do have access to matter produced in stars. After all, this is the matter of which we are composed.

The meteorites that sometimes fall to Earth are an even purer sample of the ash from exploding stars. Using data from meteorites and from the spectra of stars, astronomers and nuclear physicists have achieved an understanding of how the stars produce both heat and new elements. Many remarkable and surprising processes have been discovered and behind them all is the guiding hand of the nuclear energy valley.

Cosmic nuclear explosion: the aftermath

The effects of energetic nuclear processes in stars are still with us, literally: we are made of the products. But the results of relatively recent activity are still on display in the heavens. **The Crab Nebula** is the visible expanding cloud of matter ejected by a Type II supernova that exploded in the year 1054. This event, 6.5 thousand light years away, was recorded by Chinese and Arab astronomers. The nebula itself is still observably expanding and is now about 5.5 light years in diameter.

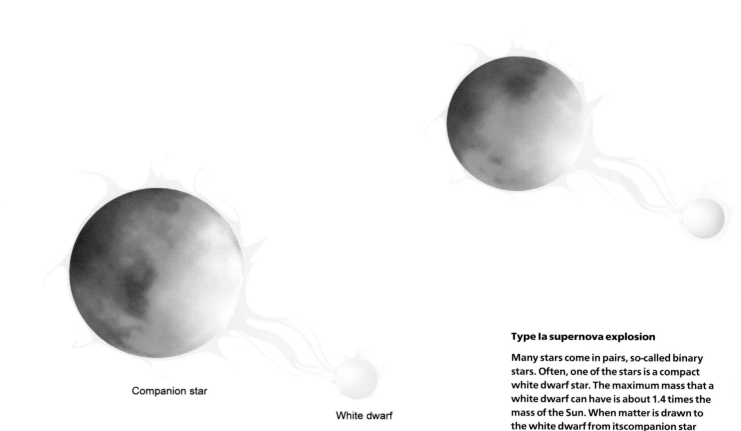

Companion star

White dwarf

Type Ia supernova explosion

Many stars come in pairs, so-called binary stars. Often, one of the stars is a compact white dwarf star. The maximum mass that a white dwarf can have is about 1.4 times the mass of the Sun. When matter is drawn to the white dwarf from its companion star and its mass is pushed over this limit, the star detonates in spectacular fashion.

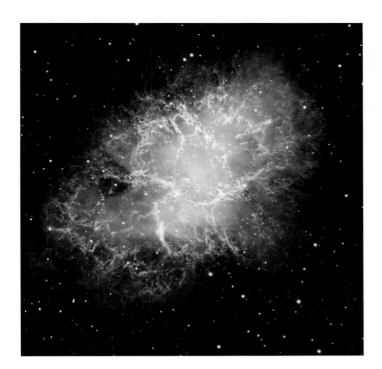

The Crab Nebula

The "Crab" is the remnant of a supernova that occurred in AD 1054 in the constellation of Taurus. At its heart is a pulsar. We now know that the pulsar is a neutron star, all that remains of the exploding star whose outer layers now fill vast regions of space. (Courtesy European Southern Observatories.)

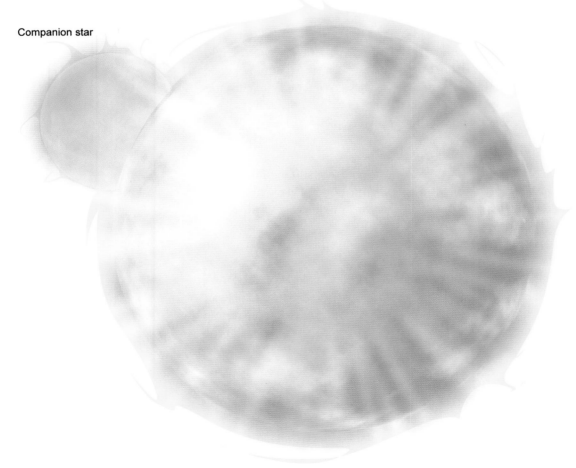

Companion star

Expanding ball of gas

10. Our violent origin

Cosmology and the nuclear processes in the Big Bang

Our Universe appears to be getting larger. The space between the galaxies is expanding so that we see distant galaxies in all directions receding from us; the more distant a galaxy is, the faster it retreats. This is not because our galaxy occupies a privileged location at the centre of the Universe; an inhabitant of another, far away, galaxy would see the same spectacle. In spite of the appearance of galaxies and clusters of galaxies, we believe that, on the largest scale, the Universe is uniform – the same everywhere.

If we imagine viewing the expansion in reverse, we can follow it all the way back to an instant, about 13.7 billion years ago, when all the matter in the Universe was squeezed together. This was the moment when space and time themselves came into being. What happened at that instant, and immediately after it, has become known as the Big Bang.

The Big Bang was an event like no other. Any attempt to describe it in terms of familiar concepts can only give a vague idea. For example, it is often referred to as an explosion of matter and energy, but this is quite wrong since the word 'explosion' suggests matter being forced out by huge pressures from a point in a pre-existing space. At the Big Bang, the whole of space itself was stretched out, carrying pure energy with it, as if it were being sucked out of nothing. The Universe did not expand into empty space; but space itself stretched tremendously.

The nature of the Big Bang is much discussed among cosmologists, but many would say that the Big Bang did not take place at some moment in time, but instead marked the very beginning of time. From that point of view, to ask what there was before the Big Bang would seem to be a meaningless question.

General relativity is currently our best theory describing the nature of space and time, and its predictions concerning motion under gravity are well supported by experiment. Our global positioning system and `SatNav' depend critically on general relativity. Its relevance here is that general relativity predicts the expansion of the Universe. Such a prediction must, of course, be supported by evidence, and evidence there is: in fact there are three independent pieces of evidence for the Big Bang.

Evidence for a Big Bang

Since all galaxies are composed of the same elements, the light emitted from distant galaxies should have the same characteristic wavelengths as that from nearer galaxies. The first evidence that the Universe is expanding is that light received from distant galaxies has a longer wavelength than when it was emitted. The spectrum of light emitted by any kind of atom is uniformly shifted to longer wavelengths. The **Light from a distant cluster of galaxies** has been shifted in this way. These increased wavelengths suggest the galaxies are receding from us at great

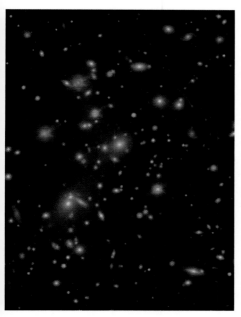

Light from a distant cluster of galaxies

The cluster of galaxies 1ES 0657-558, has taken about 6 billion years to reach us. When the light began its journey, the Universe was only about 60% of its current size. In other words, the distance between galaxies was only 60% of what it is now. Not only the Universe has stretched, the emitted light has too: wavelengths of light have increased by about 30%. Galaxies in this cluster appear 30% redder than they were when the light was emitted. (Courtesy European Southern Observatories.)

speeds. The wavelength of the light that reaches us from those galaxies is 'stretched' as the space it travels through stretches. Longer wavelengths means light is shifted towards the red end of the visible spectrum this is the cosmological red shift . This stretching of space is just the ongoing expansion of the Universe that started with the Big Bang. One way to visualize this expansion is to imagine blowing up a balloon with spots painted on it as in **The expansion**. No one spot would occupy the centre of the surface of the balloon, just as no one galaxy occupies the centre of the Universe. Concentrating on one spot and observing how other spots move in relation to it as the balloon is blown up shows every other spot recedes from it. The further away another spot, the faster it recedes, just like distant galaxies. Like all analogies, this one should not be taken too literally: the surface of the balloon is only two-dimensional. Also, the Universe is the same everywhere —- there is no special place where you 'blow into it', as you do a balloon.

The second piece of evidence for the Big Bang is the existence of microwave radiation approaching Earth from every direction in space. George Gamow first predicted the existence of this radiation long before it was actually observed. It is the 'afterglow' of the Big Bang. It has a temperature of 2.725 degrees above absolute zero (absolute zero is 273 degrees Celsius below freezing, about –459 degrees Fahrenheit), and consists of low energy photons. These photons existed about 380,000 years after the Big Bang, when the Universe had cooled to a temperature of 3000 Celsius degrees above absolute zero. At that temperature the Universe became transparent. The microwave radiation we detect is that 3000 degrees thermal radiation from that time, but now extremely red-shifted to microwave wave lengths. The red-shift is such that the wavelength has increased a thousand-fold.

The third important line of evidence comes from nuclear physics. The relative proportions of hydrogen, deuterium, and helium fit very closely with the predictions of theoretical models of the Big Bang, although there are currently some problems with lithium. However, the nuclei of these elements were not around at the very beginning. In fact, not even the protons and neutrons themselves existed at the start.

Just after the beginning

The earliest meaningful time that can be comprehended with today's physics is the unimaginably short time of 10^{-43} seconds after the Universe came into being, when the temperature was over 10^{32} degrees. At this time it was steadily expanding. At 10^{-35} seconds, the Universe that we can see now had grown to just 10^{-27} metres and the temperature had fallen to about 10^{27} degrees. At this moment it is thought that **The expansion** underwent a phenomenal acceleration. Exactly what happened is still the subject of debate among physicists, but it is believed that space itself rapidly inflated, carrying matter within it at a stupendous rate. During this 'inflation', the size of the presently visible Universe increased by a factor of at least 10^{25} from 10^{-27} metres to one centimetre (the factor may well have been as much as 10^{50} or even 10^{100}). This inflation had finished by 10^{-32} seconds. These steps are all before the second step shown in **Evolution of the Universe**.

Creating protons and neutrons

After the period of inflation, the Universe expanded at a much more sedate pace. By one millionth of a second after its birth, the temperature had fallen to below 10^{12} degrees and the nuclear ingredients, protons and neutrons, began to form.

Many properties of nucleons can be explained by assuming they are bundles of three quarks held together by gluons. The quarks come in six different types (flavours) known as 'up', 'down', 'strange', 'charm', 'top' and 'bottom'. These names are whimsical – charm quarks are not charming, for example. However,

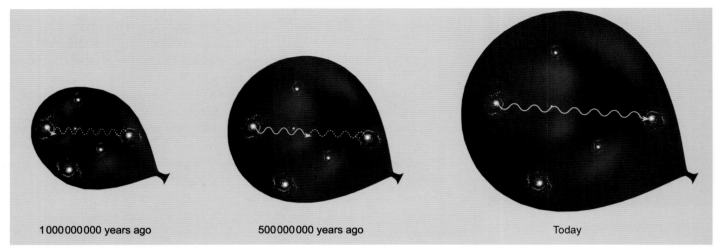

| 1 000 000 000 years ago | 500 000 000 years ago | Today |

The expansion

The expansion of three-dimensional space may be visualized as the two-dimensional surface of a balloon being inflated. As the balloon expands, everything on its surface gets further away from everything else. The wavelength of light increases as the surface area increases. A balloon is not quite spherical, and has a place where the air is blown in. Space has nothing like that. Every location is like every other, and the Big Bang was everywhere.

An image of the microwave sky by WMAP

NASA launched the Wilkinson Microwave Anisotropy Probe (WMAP) in 2001 to study the history of the Universe as revealed by microwaves. This image shows the variation in temperature of microwaves as received from point to point across the whole sky. The fluctuations in temperature of the microwaves are tiny. The colours cover a range of just a couple of hundred millionths of a degree from the otherwise very uniform 2.725 degrees Kelvin. The pattern reveals traces left by the minute density fluctuations of 13.7 billion years ago that eventually grew to become the galaxies, including our Milky Way Galaxy. (NASA) strange quarks were postulated in the 1960s as a component of certain particles discovered in 1947 known as `strange particles' since their properties were at that time inexplicable.

Nucleons are composed of just the up quarks and down quarks plus gluons. Protons consist of two up quarks, each of charge +2/3 and a down quark with charge −1/3, giving an overall charge of +1. By 'charge +2/3' we mean two thirds of the charge on a positron. Neutrons have two down quarks and one up quark, making them neutral overall. The force-carrying gluons are electrically neutral.

There are strong reasons for believing that no single free quark or free gluon will ever appear in the laboratory. If enough energy is put into a proton to knock out one of its constituent quarks, such a quark does not appear in the detectors. Instead, the energy creates a new particle that is itself made up of more than one quark. This is exactly what happens in collisions studied using particle accelerators.

The situation was different during the early Universe when all the matter was extremely compressed and hot. At one millionth of a second after the Universe came into existence, the temperature was a million, million degrees and the density of the Universe was greater than that of atomic nuclei. Under such temperatures and pressures, the boundaries between individual nucleons did not exist and quarks and gluons could move freely in a quark–gluon plasma.

As the Universe continued its expansion, and the density and temperature fell, the quarks would have begun to arrange themselves into threesomes held together by gluons, and the nucleons were formed.

A quark–gluon plasma

The brief period before one millionth of a second into the Big Bang is not the only time that the quark–gluon plasma existed. In 2000, scientists at CERN in Switzerland published evidence, gathered from many years of experiments, strongly hint-

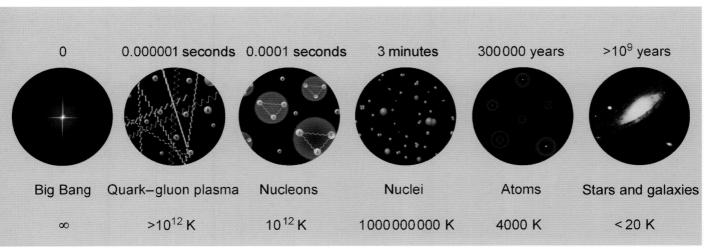

0	0.000001 seconds	0.0001 seconds	3 minutes	300 000 years	>10^9 years
Big Bang	Quark–gluon plasma	Nucleons	Nuclei	Atoms	Stars and galaxies
∞	>10^{12} K	10^{12} K	1 000 000 000 K	4000 K	< 20 K

Evolution of the Universe

Some highlights in the history of the Universe. The time along the top is the time after the instant of the Big Bang. The temperature along the bottom is the average temperature of the Universe as a whole.

ing that a quark–gluon plasma can be formed briefly when heavy nuclei collide head-on at very high energies, generating extremely high pressures and temperatures. These are just the conditions required for the boundaries between nucleons to dissolve, momentarily producing the quark–gluon plasma.

After 2000, this work continued at the Relativistic Heavy Ion Collider (RHIC) in the USA, which was built just for this purpose. In head-on collisions between gold nuclei, even higher energies were reached than had been reached at CERN. The high-density matter produced when gold nuclei collide head-on has reached a temperature of over 7 trillion degrees. The sequence of pictures shown in **Colliding gold nuclei** represents a simulation of a head-on collision between two gold nuclei at ultra-relativistic energies.

The RHIC experiments have taught us much about this ultra-hot, ultra high-density matter, and some surprising properties, not originally expected of a quark-gluon plasma, have emerged. It is intriguing to think that perhaps this unique state of matter has been produced just twice in the history of the Universe: first about a millionth of a second into the existence of the Universe, and then again briefly on planet Earth, 13.7 billion years later. In November 2010, the Large Hadron Collider, LHC, at CERN, was switched over from head-on proton-proton collisions to head-on collisions between lead nuclei at much higher energies than are possible at RHIC. There are high hopes that we shall be rewarded with new insights and surprises concerning the properties of 'nuclear stuff' as it was in the brief moment before there were nuclei, or even protons and neutrons. Everything about our present Universe depends on what happened just a millionth of a second after the first instant of the Big Bang. In **QGP at the LHC** you see an event picture of particles produced when two lead nuclei collide head-on at the energies of the LHC.

Making the light elements

When protons and neutrons first emerged from the plasma, less than a second after the first instant of the Big Bang, they attracted each other through the nuclear force but they did not yet bind together to form deuterons. This was because the temperature was still too high. For every nucleon there would have been several billion gamma ray photons that would have caused the disintegration of any deuterons as soon as they formed. Nuclei had to wait until the Universe was one second old before they could make even a fleeting appearance. At this time,

Colliding gold nuclei
From left to right, 1: two gold nuclei approach each other from opposite directions. They appear flattened because of relativistic length contraction in the direction of motion. 2: the nuclei collide, leading to the formation of a region of immense density and temperature in the laboratory frame. The pancake shape is no longer a matter of relativistic contraction in this frame. 3: the hot plasma begins to expand as a few of the nucleons pass straight through. 4.: Quarks and gluons have condensed into an expanding fireball of protons, neutrons and many other subatomic particles. (RHIC)

the temperature had dropped to 10 billion degrees, but even at this temperature, deuterons are so flimsy that they are broken up almost immediately.

After about one minute, the Universe was cool enough for the deuterons to last long enough to have a reasonable chance of combining with a further proton or neutron to form a nucleus with three nucleons: either the hydrogen isotope ^{3}H (tritium), or the helium isotope ^{3}He. Both these light nuclei resist breaking up and can readily absorb a nucleon to form the much more stable ^{4}He nucleus.

The nuclear reactions leading to ^{4}He took place in a rapidly changing environment. The density was falling fast as the Universe expanded, so nuclei collided less frequently. The rapid drop in temperature meant that there was less energy for charged nuclei to tunnel through the barrier between them. Neutrons, being uncharged, have the advantage of not having to tunnel through the barrier caused by the electric repulsion of the nuclei, but they have the disadvantage that they steadily undergo beta decay, in which they become protons.

The falling density and temperature, and the lack of free neutrons meant that nuclear fusion reactions ceased after a few minutes and no more new nuclei could be made. The primordial matter formed a few minutes after the first instant of the Big Bang had just a small number of isotopes in proportions that remained fixed for

QGP at the LHC

A high resolution "event picture" from the ALICE detector at the Large Hadron Collider. It records the particles produced when two lead nuclei collide head on. (CERN)

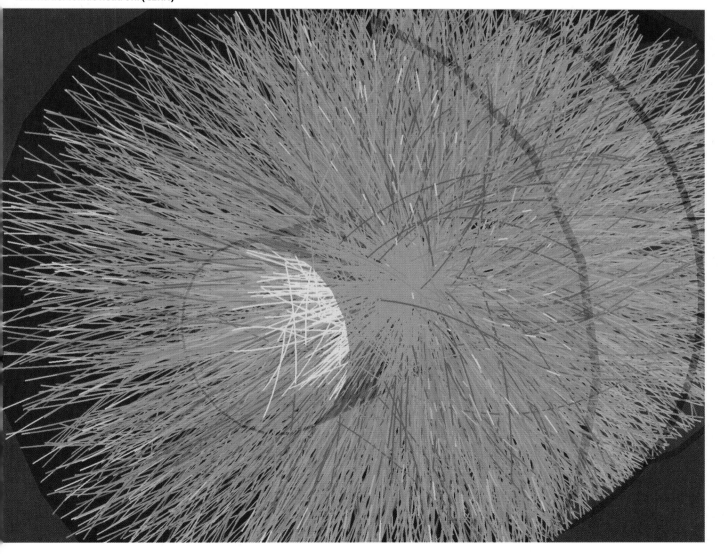

many millions of years. Only when stars began to form did other quite different element-making processes occur.

The proportions of the primordial isotopes can be predicted by theory. The overwhelming part (76% by mass) consisted of hydrogen (single protons) with the remainder (24% by mass, or about 9% by number of atoms) being helium (two protons and two neutrons). There were also tiny, but significant, traces of other isotopes: a few tens of parts per million consisted of deuterium, slightly less of the helium isotope ^{3}He, and just a tenth of a part per billion of the lithium isotope ^{7}Li. No stable nuclei with five nucleons exist in nature, and the only stable nucleus with 6 nucleons (^{6}Li) had to wait until much later to be formed. The BBN (Big Bang nucleogenesis) theory that predicts these proportions is important for another reason: it predicts the total density of baryonic material in the Universe. Baryonic material is the ordinary material made of protons, neutrons and electrons, mostly visible as stars.

The predictions of the BBN theory depend upon the density both of matter and photons at the time the processes were taking place. Most of the predictions can be tested in modern astronomical observations. For instance, ^{7}Li can be detected at the surface of very old stars lying at the edge of our galaxy which have not been contaminated by the ashes of exploding stars, and the amount of deuterium can be measured by the absorption of light from very distant galaxies as it passes through clouds of primordial gas that have not yet condensed into stars. The proportions of ^{1}H, ^{2}H and ^{4}He fit well with theory, but there are some unsolved disparities with the amount of ^{7}Li, although this last is subject to many uncertainties arising from its subsequent processing in stars.

There are no possible Big Bang processes that could lead to the formation of nuclei heavier than ^{7}Li. Yet these are necessary for the rich and complex world in which we live or for the evolution of life. The world we see around us has been made possible by the billions of years of nuclear reactions occurring within stars, described in the previous chapter. Consequently, today there is somewhat less hydrogen (70% by mass) than there was in the early Universe, while the amount of ^{4}He has increased to 28% due to stellar fusion. In addition, a vital 2% of heavier elements has appeared, making this book, its authors and its readers, possible.

The Big Bang, nucleon density and modern cosmology

Many questions remain unanswered: will the Universe expand forever or will the expansion stop some day, to be followed by contraction ending with a Big Crunch? The last now seems very unlikely since it was discovered in 1998 that the expansion of the Universe is actually accelerating. Cosmologists debate these questions intensely and a key factor is just how much matter exists in the Universe. Astronomers find this a very difficult question to answer, but the abundance of primordial isotopes provides a clue. The present density of nucleons in the Universe depends on the density of matter and radiation at the time the primordial elements were being formed, and nuclear physics provides the basis of the BBN models mentioned above.

Nuclear processes that took place in the first few minutes, in particular the amount of deuterium that was produced, depended crucially on how densely concentrated the nucleons were. The deuterium in existence today is primordial – made in the first few minutes after the Big Bang. This is known because any new deuterium created by reactions within stars is immediately destroyed by further reactions. Thus, if the amount of deuterium in existence today is measured, we can learn about the conditions at the time the primordial elements were made, which in turn provides a clue as to how much total matter there is today.

It turns out that the amount of deuterium is not exactly what is expected, but very close. Today, the BBN models based on nuclear physics have been refined to the point where their predictions are accepted. And what do these models give for the proportion of baryonic material in the Universe? They tell us that only about 5 % of the mass-energy in the Universe is baryonic, and this is in accord with observations. (We speak of mass-energy since mass and energy are equivalent according to relativity theory.)

The precise contributions of different components of the Universe are likely to be amended slightly in the coming years as observations progress. At present, it appears that about 5 % is 'ordinary' matter, about 23 % is 'cold dark matter' and about 72 % is variously called 'dark energy' or 'quintessence'. There are currently many experiments searching for cold dark matter, which interacts very weakly with ordinary matter (it is called 'cold' because the particles are thought to be quite massive and move at much less than the speed of light.) Evidence for its existence comes from astronomical observations such as the motion of stars within galaxies. The nature of dark energy is more the subject of speculative theories at present. The various percentages quoted here depend particularly upon precise observations of the way that the cosmic microwave background varies with direction. The variations are astoundingly small: about one part in 100 000.

The 'ordinary matter' is not entirely baryonic: although most of the 5% is hydrogen and helium, about 0.3 % is neutrinos, and just 0.03 % is made up of all the heavier elements.

These are exciting times, and nuclear physicists, astronomers and cosmologists, working together, will refine our models in the coming years, probably with some profound surprises. We can be sure of establishing a firmer understanding of the history of the Universe and also of its future.

At the beginning of Chapter 1 we showed a diagram that suggested that what we have learned about Nature on the very smallest scale somehow 'joins up' with what we have learned on the largest scale. Nuclear and particle physics and cosmology feed into each other. This last chapter has hopefully given some hints of how this comes about.

Further reading

The Magic Furnace: The Search for the Origins of Atoms, Marcus Chown (Oxford University Press, 2001)
A very readable and eloquent historical account of how scientists unravelled the mystery of atoms. It chronicles the achievements of the pioneers of atomic and nuclear physics.

From X-rays to Quarks, Emilio Segrè (W. H. Freeman, 1976)
A first hand account of the history of modern nuclear and particle physics by the Nobel Prize winning student of Fermi. Most likely to be found in a library.

Enrico Fermi Physicist, Emilio Segrè (Chicago University Press, 1995)
A readable account of the life and works of Fermi by his distinguished student.

The Nature of Matter, J. H. Mulvey (ed.) (Clarendon Press, 1981)
A series of lectures by front rank physicists delivered at Wolfson College, Oxford. Most of the lectures are not too technical, and some are very inspiring.

Atom: Journey Across the Subatomic Cosmos, Isaac Asimov (Penguin, 1992)
The legendary Isaac Asimov starts with a simple query: How finely can a piece of matter be divided? This leads readers on a far-flung quest for a final answer, a search that encompasses light and electricity and their components - strange bits of matter that challenge our assumptions about the very nature of time and space.

The First Three Minutes: A Modern View of the Origin of the Universe, Steven Weinberg (Basic Books, 1993)
A classic of contemporary popular science writing by a Nobel Prize winning physicist explains what happened when the Universe began, and how we know.

Bang! The Complete History of the Universe, Brian May, Patrick Moore, and Chris Lintott (Carlton/Johns Hopkins, paperback 2009)

The Dark Side of the Universe, Iain Nicolson (Canopus/Johns Hopkins, second edition 2010)

Nuclear Physics: Principles and Applications, John Lilley (John Wiley, 2001)
Although this is an undergraduate textbook, it is an excellent source for applications of nuclear physics, particularly in medicine.

Quantum: A Guide for the Perplexed, Jim Al-Khalili (Weidenfeld & Nicolson, paperback 2004)

Atom, Jim Al-Khalili and Piers Bizony (Icon Books, 2007)

Useful websites

Nuclear Physics Laboratories around the world
GSI (Darmstadt, Germany) http://www.gsi.de/
GANIL (Caen, France) http://www.ganil.fr/
CERN (Geneva, Switzerland) http://www.cern.ch/
RHIC (Brookhaven, USA) http://www.bnl.gov/rhic/
Jefferson Lab (Virginia, USA) http://www.jlab.org
Argonne National Lab (Argonne, USA) http://www.anl.gov/
Lawrence Berkeley Lab (Berkeley, USA) http://www.lbl.gov/
TRIUMF (Vancouver, Canada): http://www.triumf.ca/
National Superconducting Cyclotron Laboratory (East Lansing, USA) http://www.nscl.msu.edu/
RIKEN (Saitama, Japan) http://tinyurl.com/6g1752y
CRC (Louvain la Neuve, Belgium) http://www.cyc.ucl.ac.be/
KVI (Groningen, Netherlands) http://www.kvi.nl/
ANU (Canberra, Australia): http://physics.anu.edu.au/nuclear
JINR (Dubna, Russia): http://www.jinr.dubna.su/
INFN (Legnaro, Italy) http://www.lnl.infn.it/
TSL (Uppsala, Sweden) http://www.tsl.uu.se/
JYFL (Jyvaskyla, Finland) http://www.phys.jyu.fi/research/
ORNL (Oak Ridge, USA) http://www.ornl.gov

Nuclear Fusion Power
JET (Culham UK) http://www.jet.efd.org/
ITER (International) http://www.iter.org/

Physics Institutes and Societies
Institute of Physics (IoP) (UK): http://www.iop.org/
American Physical Society (APS) (USA): http://www.aps.org/

Nuclear Energy
Nuclear Technology Education Consortium (NTEC): http://ntec.ac.uk

Glossary

Italic type indicates terms with a separate glossary entry

Alpha particle: The nucleus of the helium atom containing two protons and two neutrons. It is a highly stable nucleus and is emitted in one piece from many heavier nuclei in a process known as alpha decay. Alpha particles were known before it was understood that they comprised of *protons* and *neutrons*. They are also doubly ionized helium atoms, that is helium atoms with both electrons removed.

Anti-matter: matter made up entirely of anti-particles.

Anti-particle: a type of subatomic particle that is like a mirror image of the original particle in that many of its key properties are reversed. For instance, the anti-proton has the same mass as the *proton* but is negatively charged. When particles and their corresponding anti-particles meet, they mutually annihilate each other in a burst of energy. Similarly, a particle and anti-particle pair can be created out of pure energy. The anti-electron is known as a *positron*, and has a positive charge with the same magnitude as the negative charge on an *electron*.

Atomic mass unit (amu): the conventional unit for expressing the mass of nuclei. It is one twelfth of the mass of a neutral carbon atom, ^{12}C. The mass of a nucleus in amu is approximately equal to the mass number of a nucleus.

Atomic number: symbol Z, the number of *protons* in a nucleus. Also the total number of *electrons* in a neutral atom, since if the charges are to balance, the number of electrons outside the nucleus must equal the number of protons in the nucleus.

Baryons: *hadrons* that are composed of three *quarks*. The lightest baryons are the *protons* and *neutrons*. Heavier hadrons, such as the *delta particle*, are unstable. Baryons and *mesons* (which contain just a quark and an anti-quark) make up the two types of hadron.

Beta decay: the process, governed by the weak nuclear force, whereby *protons* and *neutrons* can transform into each other. When a neutron beta decays, an *electron* and an anti-neutrino are released. A free neutron can beta decay because its mass exceeds the sum of the proton and electron masses. A proton can only beta decay within a nucleus with excess energy and becomes a *positron* plus a *neutrino*; this happens within nuclei with a sufficient excess of protons.

Beta ray: the old name given to the *electrons*, or *positrons*, emitted from nuclei in the process of *beta decay*.

Borromean nucleus: a certain type of unstable nucleus that acts as though it is made up of three distinct parts. The bulk of the nucleus makes up the core, while two *nucleons* (usually *neutrons*) 'float' around outside it. These three constituents (core plus two nucleons) are held together very weakly by the strong nuclear force in such a way that if any one of them is removed then the force between the remaining two is too weak to hold them together and they too fall apart. This behaviour is unique in Nature. The term Borromean comes from the field of mathematics known as knot theory in which the Borromean rings are interlocked such that each one holds the other two together. Examples of Borromean nuclei are ^{6}He, ^{11}Li and ^{14}Be, all of which are also *halo nuclei*.

Bubble chamber: a device for revealing the paths of charged (highly *ionizing*) particles as they pass through a 'super-saturated' liquid. Sometimes a liquid, such as liquid hydrogen, can be heated above its boiling point if it is very pure. However, a charged particle passing through such a 'super-saturated' liquid will leave a series of bubbles at the points where the particle ionized the liquid.

Chain reaction: when a uranium nucleus is induced to undergo *fission* by the absorption of a neutron, it will itself release a few *neutrons*. These can then in turn induce other nuclei to undergo fission, and so on, throughout a significant volume of uranium. This is a neutron chain reaction.

Cloud chamber: a device for revealing the paths of charged (highly *ionizing*) particles as they pass through 'saturated' water vapour. There is a limit to the amount of water vapour air can hold, but that limit can sometimes be exceeded. A charged particle passing through such a 'saturated' vapour will leave a series of droplets at the points where the particle ionized the vapour.

Cyclotron: an accelerator for charged particles in which the particles are held in a spiral orbit in a vacuum chamber by a magnetic field, and given a series of pushes by an electric field.

Delta particle: a relation of the *nucleon*, this particle can be thought of as an *excited state* of the nucleon with a slightly greater mass.

Diffraction: the property of all waves whereby they spread out on encountering a obstacle. The amount of spreading depends on the *frequency* of the wave and the size of the object.

Driplines: these are the limits on a Segrè chart beyond which nuclei do not exist. So-called because it is as if nucleons inserted into such a nucleus drip straight out again.

Electromagnetic radiation: any radiation consisting of self-sustaining electric and magnetic fields. All electromagnetic radiation travels in a vacuum with the same speed: the speed of light. Light, radio waves, ultraviolet, gamma and infrared radiation are fundamentally the same, differing only in *frequency* and *wavelength*. All their differing effects on matter result from the difference in frequency and hence the difference in energy of the photons.

Electron: the first elementary particle to be discovered. It belongs to the class of particles known as *leptons*. Electrons are very light negatively charged particles and are the constituents of atoms outside the nucleus. Electrons have a mass of 9×10^{-31} kg, about one two-thousandth of the mass of the lightest atom, the hydrogen atom. They have zero size and so are considered to be 'point particles'. They are the carrier of electricity in metals.

Electron capture: the process in which an *electron* is absorbed by a nucleus wherein it combines with a *proton* to make a *neutron* and a *neutrino*.

Energy levels: the allowed discrete (quantized) values of energy that a nucleus can have. Each kind of nucleus has a unique pattern of energy levels. Atoms and molecules also have unique patterns of energy levels.

Energy valley (nuclear): not all nuclei have the same amount of energy per nucleon. If all nuclei are arranged according to N and Z, as in a *Segrè chart*, and a line is raised from the position of each nucleus, proportional to the energy per nucleon, then the tops of those lines will form a surface taking the appearance of a valley. The stable nuclei will be those near the bottom of the valley. The nuclei higher up the valley will undergo radioactive transformations, losing energy and sliding down the sides of the valley.

Excited state: any *energy level* of a nucleus above its *ground state*.

Fission: the process whereby a heavy nucleus splits into two roughly equal smaller nuclei, releasing energy locked up inside it. Usually, fission takes place after a nucleus has been stimulated by the absorption of a *neutron*, but *spontaneous fission* does exist. Fission is the process that produces nuclear power through controlled chain reactions.

Frequency: the number of vibrations of an oscillating system that occur in one second. For the case of waves, it is the number of wave crests that pass by a fixed point in one second. It is measured in Hertz (= cycles per second).

Fusion: the nuclear process whereby two light nuclei can overcome the mutual electric (Coulomb) repulsion to fuse together. This is accompanied by the release of a large amount of energy and is the source of energy in the Sun and other stars. It is hoped that fusion will one day be harnessed as an energy source on Earth.

Gamma ray: a high energy *photon* (particle of light) released from within atomic nuclei when they find themselves in an unstable excited state. Gamma rays can also be absorbed by nuclei which then become excited.

Gluon: massless particle, never seen isolated outside *hadrons*, which generate the attraction between the *quarks* within the hadrons, holding them together.

Ground state: the lowest *energy level* of a nucleus (or atom).

Hadrons: all particles that interact via the strong nuclear force. Hadrons are composed of *quarks*; *protons* and *neutrons* are hadrons, as are *mesons*.

Half life: the time after which half of a large collection of identical radioactive nuclei will have decayed.

Halo nucleus: a certain type of exotic nucleus discovered in the mid 1980s that has many more *neutrons* than the stable *isotope* of that element. This sometimes results in the outer one or two neutrons being very weakly linked to the rest of the nucleons and thus they spend much of their time far beyond the range of the strong nuclear force that originally bound them to the rest of the nucleus. Such nuclei are highly unstable and only exist due to strange rules of quantum mechanics. Examples of one neutron halo nuclei are ^{11}Be and ^{19}C, while two-neutron halo nuclei tend to be *Borromean*. Nuclei with *proton* halos also exist (such as ^{8}B) but in that case the repulsion between the proton's positive charge and the rest of the nucleus means that it cannot stray very far out or it falls out. Thus proton halos tend to be smaller than neutron halos.

Interference: a property of waves whereby two waves overlap each other to produce a pattern of maxima (when two wave crests meet and combine) and minima (when a wave crest meets a wave trough and they cancel out). The pattern of dark and light that results allows us to learn about the waves and about the system in which interference takes place.

Ion: an atom, or molecule, which is no longer electrically neutral, usually because one or more *electrons* have been knocked out, but the term can apply to an atom with an extra electron (negative ion).

Ionize: the process of removing *electrons* from atoms or molecules so that they are no longer electrically neutral. *Alpha*, *beta* and *gamma rays* ionize the atoms of matter with which they interact.

Isobar: *nuclides* with different numbers of *protons* and *neutrons* but the same total number of protons plus neutrons, i.e. the same atomic *mass number*.

Isomer: a nucleus that is in a long-lived excited state (called an isomeric state or a metastable state). Certain nuclei can remain in such excited states due to certain quantum properties they have which forbid them from dropping down to a lower *energy level* by emitting gamma rays.

Isotones: *nuclides* with the same number of *neutrons* but different numbers of *protons*.

Isotope: all *nuclides* of a particular element (having the same number of *protons*) but with different numbers of neutrons are known as isotopes of that element. Thus ^{12}C and ^{14}C are different isotopes of carbon.

Isotope shift: the optical spectrum of an atom depends almost entirely on the *electrons* outside the nucleus, but the size of the nucleus does have a tiny but measurable effect. This means that careful measurements of the optical spectra of atoms allow us to measure the size of the nucleus. This is very useful for nuclei that live for too short a time for measurements based on electron scattering to be made.

Leptons: one of the two classes of elementary particles in nature. They include the *electron*, muon and tau particle, along with their corresponding *neutrinos*.

Linear accelerator: an accelerator for charged particles in which the particles are given a series of pushes down a long straight vacuum chamber by oscillating electric fields.

Magic number: particular numbers of *protons* or *neutrons* lead to nuclei with increased stability compared to the neighbouring nuclei. For neutrons these numbers are 2, 8, 20, 28, 50, 82 and 126. They are the same for protons except that no nucleus with 126 protons is known.

Mass number: symbol A, the total number of *protons* and *neutrons* in a nucleus. $A = N + Z$, where N is the number of neutrons and Z is the number of protons.

Meson: subatomic particle that can be considered as the carrier of the strong nuclear force between *nucleons* in nuclei. There are various types of mesons and they can be neutral, positively or negatively charged. It is now known that mesons are, like nucleons, themselves composed of *quarks*. But unlike nucleons, which are made up of three *quarks*, mesons contain a quark and an anti-quark.

Neutrino: an effectively massless particle emitted during *beta decay*. Its name means 'little neutral one' and until recently was thought to have no mass at all (like the *photon*). It is now known that there are three types of neutrinos, along with their corresponding anti-particles, but it is the lightest of these that is emitted by nuclei.

Neutron: the other constituent, along with *protons*, of nuclei; it has a mass very slightly greater than the proton but is electrically neutral. Neutrons cannot survive for long outside the confines of the nucleus and they *beta decay*, that is turn into protons and anti-neutrinos, after about ten minutes.

Neutron star: the compact corpse left behind when a giant star dies in a *supernova* explosion. It has much the same density as a nucleus. Many experiments are aimed at understanding enough of the properties of *nuclear matter* at high pressures to enable us to understand neutron stars.

Nuclear matter: broadly speaking, the stuff of nuclei. It is because nuclear matter is incompressible that the density of *nucleons* at the centre of nuclei is much the same for all nuclei except the very lightest. For the same reason, neutron stars have much the same density as we find at the centre of nuclei.

Nucleon: general term for either a *proton* or a *neutron*.

Nuclide: a nucleus of a given number of *protons* and *neutrons*. There are about 7000 different possible nuclides, only several hundred of which are stable.

Oblate deformation: the deformation of a sphere that is achieved by squeezing two sides together. The Earth is slightly oblate since it is a little squashed at the poles making the equator slightly longer than it would be if the Earth were a perfect sphere.

Photomultiplier: a very sensitive *photon* detector, capable of measuring the energy in a very weak pulse of light. It forms part of a *scintillation detector* for measuring *gamma rays*. The pulse of light is generated as a *scintillation*.

Photon: a single particle of light. Einstein proposed in 1905 that light came in packets or light quanta, as an explanation for the photoelectric effect, whereby light can knock out electrons from the surface of a metal. Together with the work of Max Planck, this marked the beginning of the old quantum theory in which light is considered to be composed of discrete lumps. Later, it was realized that these packets of light energy had the same characteristics as particles, such as appearing at a single point in detectors, and they became known as photons.

Pion: the lightest *meson*, with mass of about one seventh of the *nucleon* mass.

Positron: the anti-particle of the *electron*. It has the same mass as the electron but with opposite (positive) electric charge. The beta radiation from nuclei consists of electrons or positrons together with the (very nearly) undetectable *neutrinos*.

Prolate deformation: the deformation of a sphere into the shape of an 'American football' shape. This can be achieved with a balloon, say, by pulling apart two points on either side of the balloon's surface.

Proton: one of the constituents of nuclei and the only constituent of the lightest nucleus, hydrogen. It has a positive charge of the same magnitude as the negative charge on an *electron*, and a mass almost two thousand times heavier than the electron. Every neutral atom contains as many protons in its nucleus as electrons orbiting outside it.

Quantum mechanics: the set of physical laws that govern the behaviour of the subatomic world. It began with the ideas of Max Planck and Albert Einstein at the beginning of the twentieth century and was developed into a complete mathematical theory by the mid-1920s by Neils Bohr, Erwin Schrödinger and Werner Heisenberg. Other physicists such as Paul Dirac, Max Born and Wolfgang Pauli made major contributions. While quantum mechanics is the most successful theory in science, underpinning much of modern physics, chemistry, electronics and material science, its predictions remain strange and counter-intuitive, especially when met for the first time.

Quark: component particle of *protons*, *neutrons*, *mesons* and other *hadrons*. They cannot exist isolated, outside hadrons. The proton consists of two 'up' quarks, each with a positive charge of magnitude 2/3 the charge of an electron, and one 'down' quark, with a negative charge 1/3 the charge of an electron; the neutron has two down quarks and one up quark, making it a neutral particle.

Quark–gluon plasma: when *nuclear matter* is raised to a high temperature and subjected to huge pressure, as happens in very high energy collisions between heavy nuclei, the boundaries between the *nucleons* disappear and the *quarks* and *gluons* within them form a sort of soup. The Universe very briefly passed through a quark–gluon phase before *protons* and *neutrons* emerged after the Big Bang.

Scintillation: the flash of light when a nuclear particle or *gamma ray* strikes certain substances.

Scintillation counter: a particle detector in which the light from *scintillations* is detected and measured with *photomultipliers*.

Segrè chart: a chart of the nuclei arranged (usually) with the *proton* number on the vertical axis and the *neutron* number on the horizontal axis. Generally, the square on this chart which corresponds to particular values of N and Z will indicate key properties of that particular nucleus, such as its radioactivity.

Silicon detector: modern detectors of charged particles are based on the fact that such particles cause electrical signals to be generated when they pass through or are absorbed. Such detectors allow the energies and directions of particles produced in nuclear reactions to be measured accurately.

Spallation: when a very high energy *proton* or other projectile strikes a nucleus, the nucleus is likely to shatter, producing an array of lighter nuclei. Nuclei such as ^{6}Li are believed to have been produced in spallation reactions in interstellar space.

Spectrometer: an instrument that separates radiation into its different *wavelengths* (or *frequencies*). Since every nucleus or every different atom radiates different sets of wavelengths, a spectrometer allows us to identify what atoms or nuclei are present in a sample. In addition, the particular pattern of wavelengths provides vital information about the atom or nucleus from which it has been radiated.

Spectrum: a representation showing how the strength (or brightness) of *electromagnetic radiation* from a given source depends on its *wavelength*. Also refers to the band of colours we see when light or other radiation is separated according to *frequency* (or wavelength); the most familiar example of this is the rainbow spectrum of visible light.

Spontaneous fission: the process whereby a heavy nucleus with an excess of neutrons splits roughly in half into two lighter nuclei. Such a process is a type of radioactive decay and takes place without the nucleus needing to absorb any surplus neutrons to prompt it to *fission* as would be needed in a nuclear reactor.

Super-heavy nuclei: nuclei with Z in the region of 110 or above.

Supernova, type Ia and type II: a supernova is the catastrophic explosion of a star in which it briefly emits as much radiation as all the stars in its galaxy. A type Ia supernova takes place when the companion to a white dwarf star sheds enough matter onto the white dwarf that it exceeds the maximum mass such a star can have. A type II supernova takes place when the nuclear fuel in a giant star is exhausted. Radiation pressure from nuclear reactions can no longer hold the star up, so it collapses inwards. It then bounces out as a result of the incompressibility of *nuclear matter*, releasing vast amounts of energy, a flood of *neutrinos* and much matter into space.

Many elements of which we and the Solar System are made were produced in supernova explosions billions of years ago.

Synchrotron: developed from the *cyclotron* for much higher energies and involving a circular rather than spiral path. Synchrotrons can accelerate charged particles to very nearly the speed of light.

Theory of relativity: Einstein's special theory is based on two ideas: (i) that the speed of light in a vacuum (c) is always the same, no matter how fast you are moving relative to the source of light, and (ii) the laws of physics are the same no matter how fast your lab is moving at a steady speed. One consequence is that mass m and energy E are equivalent, and that $E = mc^2$.

Tokamak: an apparatus for producing nuclear *fusion* on Earth. It consists of a vacuum chamber in the form of a torus together with large magnets for keeping the interacting ions on closed paths through the vacuum.

Tunnelling (quantum): *quantum mechanics* permits particles to appear on the far side of barriers which, according to physics before quantum mechanics, they would not have the energy to surmount. This 'quantum tunnelling' controls such things as *alpha decay*, and permits the *fusion* of light nuclei in stars, allowing stars like the Sun to shine for billions of years.

Uncertainty Principle: one of the fundamental ideas in quantum theory, first expressed by the German physicist Werner Heisenberg, which states that for any object certain pairs of properties, such as position and momentum, cannot be known precisely at the same time. However, this feature is not a result of the inevitable 'clumsiness' of our measuring apparatus when it comes to subatomic objects, but rather is inherent in the objects themselves.

Wavelength: the distance between two consecutive crests (or troughs) of a wave; wavelength is inversely proportional to the frequency of the wave. For electromagnetic radiation, the wavelength is equal to the speed of light divided by the frequency.

Wave–particle duality: the quantum concept whereby both matter and radiation must be regarded at their most fundamental level as sometimes having wave properties and sometimes particle properties. For example, *electrons* and *photons* sometimes behave like particles and sometimes like waves.

X-ray: a form of electromagnetic radiation with *wavelengths* shorter than ultraviolet but longer than *gamma rays*. Since the wavelength of the radiation is related to energy this means that X-ray photons are less energetic than gamma ray photons. However, there is no sharp dividing line between the two. X-rays have wavelengths ranging from about 10 nanometres down to 10 picometers (see table on page 16).

Subject index

Bold type indicates an illustration

Name index

Bold type indicates a photograph